THE BIBLE QUESTION BEE

by

PAUL N. ELBIN, Ph.D.
President, West Liberty State College

ASSOCIATION PRESS
New York: 347 Madison Avenue

FLEMING H. REVELL COMPANY
New York: 158 Fifth Avenue

1943

COPYRIGHT, 1943, BY
THE INTERNATIONAL COMMITTEE OF
YOUNG MEN'S CHRISTIAN ASSOCIATIONS

 145

PRINTED IN THE UNITED STATES OF AMERICA

Preface

THE VARIOUS USES of *The Bible Question Bee* are rather obvious. The questions and answers of several types, the incomplete statements and quotations, the multiple choices, and the biographical exercises are all intended to make attractive the often dull process of reviewing the Bible. In Sunday schools, week-day schools of religious education, vacation church schools, young people's organizations, "socials" or parties, public schools, and homes, *The Bible Question Bee* may provide a means of learning along with entertainment. Contests between classes or among various groups of almost any age may be arranged.

For six years I have conducted a weekly Bible Question Bee on WWVA, the Blue Network radio station in Wheeling, West Virginia. The material in this volume has been interesting to radio audiences. Little question bees, using questions previously heard on the radio program, have sprung up in hundreds of communities, and the material has thus received additional criticism. Two previous editions of *The Bible Question Bee* were printed to meet the needs of these local groups.

The questions are non-controversial, purposely avoiding references to peculiarities of church doctrine or to varieties of Biblical interpretation. For the most part, they concern well-known Bible characters, incidents, or quotations. The convenience of having the answers immediately follow the questions has been proved again and again by teachers, ministers, party leaders, and parents who have used the questions. The correct answer for each question is given in italics.

3

I hope that the publication of this material will increase widely the popularity of Bible question bees. Not only are they entertaining, but they provide a good way of getting acquainted with that book without a knowledge of which no one is educated.

PAUL N. ELBIN

West Liberty State College,
West Liberty, West Virginia

Contents

1. Which Is Correct?

THE FOLLOWING STATEMENTS contain one or more errors of fact. Either repeat the statement with all errors corrected, or point out the mistakes, making the proper corrections. The corrected statements follow in italics:

1. Hosea, one of the lesser known disciples of Jesus, wrote the book bearing his name.

Hosea, one of the Hebrew prophets, wrote the book bearing his name.

2. The Book of James, possibly written by a brother of Jesus, is not found in the Roman Catholic version of the Bible.

The Book of James, possibly written by a brother of Jesus, is found in all versions of the Bible.

3. Jeremiah, one of the faithful helpers of Paul, was born before the birth of Jesus.

Jeremiah, one of the great Hebrew prophets, was born about six hundred years before the birth of Jesus.

4. Thomas, being one of the twelve disciples, was one who never questioned the resurrection of Jesus.

Thomas, although one of the twelve disciples, nevertheless questioned the resurrection of Jesus.

5. Palestine is situated on the east coast of Africa and is unimportant in history except for the birth of Jesus.

Palestine is situated at the extreme eastern end of the Mediterranean Sea and has figured prominently in history for at least three thousand years. Jesus was born at Bethlehem.

6. The Mount of Olives will always be remembered be-

cause it was the scene of the giving of the Ten Commandments to Moses.

The Mount of Olives will always be remembered because it was the scene of the ascension of Jesus. The Ten Commandments were given on Mount Sinai.

7. Mount Pisgah is remembered because from its summit Noah watched the flood waters recede.

Mount Pisgah is remembered because from its summit Moses viewed the Promised Land. The Ark landed on Mount Ararat.

8. Elisha, whose career was totally devoid of the miraculous, was preceded in the prophetic ministry by Joshua, a noted poet.

Elisha, whose career was filled with miraculous happenings, was preceded in the prophetic ministry by Elijah— not Joshua, who was a military leader.

9. Although Jesus was born in Nazareth, he spent very little time there.

Jesus was born in Bethlehem, but he spent most of the first thirty years of his life in Nazareth.

10. John the Baptist proclaimed his message on the streets of Jerusalem, but his message never interested anyone of importance.

John the Baptist proclaimed his message in the wilderness from the banks of the river Jordan, and he interested many, including Jesus.

11. Jesus spent most of his life in Judea, but only one of his disciples was a Judean.

Jesus spent most of his life in Galilee, and all of his disciples but one (Judas) were Galileans.

12. Luke followed the writing of the Gospel that bears his name by writing the Epistle to the Hebrews.

Luke followed the writing of the Gospel that bears his name by writing the Acts of the Apostles.

13. The followers of Jesus were called Christians at

Jerusalem, but the first "headquarters" of the movement were at Rome.

The followers of Jesus were first called Christians at Antioch, but the first "headquarters" of the movement were at Jerusalem.

14. Abraham and Isaac were the rulers chiefly responsible for the development and beautification of Jerusalem.

David and Solomon were the rulers chiefly responsible for the development and beautification of Jerusalem.

15. Elizabeth, sister of the mother of Jesus, was the mother of John, the beloved disciple.

Elizabeth, cousin of the mother of Jesus, was the mother of John the Baptist.

16. Jesus was born in Bethany, where Mary and Joseph had gone to build a new home.

Jesus was born in Bethlehem, where Mary and Joseph had gone to register for tax purposes.

17. When Jesus raised Leviticus from the dead, the man's sisters, Miriam and Mary, were absent from the scene.

When Jesus raised Lazarus from the dead, Lazarus' sisters, Mary and Martha, were present.

18. Jesus was thirty years of age when he first saw Jerusalem, capital of the Roman Empire.

Jesus was twelve years of age when he first saw Jerusalem, Jewish capital city and site of the temple (except in infancy; see Luke 2:22).

19. Throughout his ministry, Jesus was honored in Nazareth; but he always avoided Capernaum.

It appears that Jesus was never honored in Nazareth after the beginning of his ministry, but in friendly Capernaum he resided for a time.

20. The Jordan is the chief river of Palestine, and in its waters Jesus baptized many converts.

The Jordan is the chief river of Palestine, and in its waters Jesus was baptized.

21. After Joseph was sold into Assyrian captivity by his jealous brothers, his father, Abraham, grieved.

After Joseph was sold into Egyptian captivity by his jealous brothers, his father, Jacob, grieved.

22. A parable is usually an allegory based on an actual happening.

A parable is usually not an allegory; for a parable ordinarily has one obvious lesson, and the characters are not representative. The narrative framework of the parable need not be an actual happening.

23. On Mount Carmel, Elijah conducted his famous contest with the priests of Jove.

On Mount Carmel, Elijah conducted his famous contest with the priests of Baal.

24. Since Jesus was himself a Pharisee, it is surprising that he should have opposed them so frequently.

Jesus was not a Pharisee, and it was inevitable that his views should have clashed with theirs.

25. In the Garden of Gethsemane, Adam and Eve began their short-lived experiment in Utopia.

In the Garden of Eden, Adam and Eve began their short-lived experiment in Utopia.

26. Barnabus accompanied Jesus on his first missionary journey.

Barnabus accompanied Paul on his first missionary journey.

27. Following his baptism by Peter, Jesus immediately called for disciples.

Following his baptism by John, Jesus went into the wilderness alone and was tempted.

28. John the Baptist was executed by hanging at the command of Pilate, who was influenced by a dancer.

John the Baptist was executed by beheading at the command of King Herod (Antipas), who was influenced by a dancer.

10

29. In remorse for denying Jesus, Peter committed suicide and Judas wept bitterly.

In remorse for denying Jesus, Peter wept bitterly and Judas committed suicide.

30. Jonah set forth on the Sea of Galilee, rather than going to Babylonia as God had directed.

Jonah set forth on the Mediterranean Sea, rather than going to Nineveh as God had directed.

31. Saul of Tarsus, having discussed the "new birth" with Jesus by night, soon thereafter became a leading disciple.

Saul of Tarsus never saw Jesus in the flesh. (It was Nicodemus who saw Jesus by night.) Before his conversion, he was a persecutor of the followers of Jesus.

32. Ruth was the mother-in-law of Naomi, whose marriage to David she planned.

Naomi was the mother-in-law of Ruth, whose marriage to Boaz she planned.

33. Titus, an assistant of Paul, is the author of the book in the New Testament that bears his name.

Titus was one of Paul's assistants, but the Book of Titus was written by Paul.

34. Jesus is called the good shepherd because he wrote the Twenty-third Psalm.

David, not Jesus, wrote the Twenty-third Psalm. Jesus referred to himself as the good shepherd.

35. David and King Saul remained devoted to each other through their common determination to subdue the Philistines.

Although David and King Saul both fought against the Philistines, they were not friends.

36. Samuel was the last of the judges and the first king.

Samuel was the last of the judges, and Saul was the first king.

37. When Paul had finished the Sermon on the Mount, great multitudes followed him.

11

When Jesus had finished the Sermon on the Mount, great multitudes followed him.

38. When Jesus made his triumphal entry into Jericho, the crowds cried: "Hosannah to the son of Mary!"

When Jesus made his triumphal entry into Jerusalem, the crowds cried: "Hosannah to the son of David!"

39. Two murderers were crucified with Jesus, and both spoke unkind words to him.

Two thieves were crucified with Jesus. One spoke unkindly to him, but the other asked for his blessing.

40. "When I was a man, I spake as a man; but when I became old, I put away childish things."

"When I was a child, I spake as a child; but when I became a man, I put away childish things."

41. "Wine is a shocker; strong drink is enraging."

"Wine is a mocker; strong drink is raging."

42. "I was glad when they said unto me, Let us go into the house of feasting."

"I was glad when they said unto me, Let us go into the house of the Lord."

43. "Suffer the little children, and forbid them, for of such is the kingdom of Israel."

"Suffer the little children to come unto me, and forbid them not, for of such is the kingdom of God."

44. "Well done, good and faithful servant; thou hast been faithful over a few things, I will make thee captain of the army."

"Well done, good and faithful servant; thou hast been faithful over a few things, I will make thee ruler over many things."

45. "Happy is the man that findest money, and the man that getteth publicity."

"Happy is the man that findeth wisdom, and the man that getteth understanding."

46. "The fear of the mob is the beginning of trouble; but fools despise wisdom and instruction."

12

"The fear of the Lord is the beginning of knowledge; but fools despise wisdom and instruction."

47. "God put an angel with a flowing staff before the gate of the Garden of Eden."

"Flaming sword," not "flowing staff."

48. The disciples said: "Suffer the little children to come unto us, and forbid them not."

Jesus said: "Suffer the little children to come unto me, and forbid them not."

49. David was cast into a den of lions.

Daniel, not David.

50. The Lord set a mark upon Abel, lest any finding him should kill him.

The mark was put on Cain, not Abel.

51. King Solomon planned to kill the baby Jesus.

King Herod, not King Solomon.

52. The Ark was built by Moses.

By Noah, not Moses.

53. Jesus arose from the dead on Good Friday.

Jesus arose on Easter.

54. David prepared to offer his son on the altar as a sacrifice.

Abraham, not David.

55. David's friends were thrown into a fiery furnace.

Daniel's friends, not David's.

56. Jesus was baptized by the Apostle John.

He was baptized by John the Baptist.

57. Jesus was born in the city of Nazareth.

He was born in the town of Bethlehem.

58. Cain killed his brother Esau.

His brother Abel, not Esau.

59. The first verse in the Bible begins: "The earth is without form, and void."

The first verse begins: "In the beginning God created the heaven and the earth."

13

60. The shortest verse in the Bible is: "Lord, is it I?"
The shortest verse is: "Jesus wept."

61. Nebuchadnezzar was the oldest man recorded in the Bible.
Methuselah, not Nebuchadnezzar.

62. Many of the Psalms were written by Paul.
David, not Paul.

63. Revelations is the last book in the Bible.
Revelation, not Revelations.

64. Jonah was swallowed by a lion.
By a whale or "great fish," not a lion.

65. Samson's strength lay in his arms.
In his hair, not his arms.

66. Esau and Jacob were the first brothers mentioned in the Bible.
Cain and Abel were the first brothers mentioned.

67. When the King of Sheba visited King David, he said that not one quarter of the greatness of the Hebrew king's wisdom had been told him.
When the Queen of Sheba visited King Solomon, she said that not one half of the greatness of the Hebrew king's wisdom had been told her.

68. When three of David's men brought him water from the well of Jerusalem, he insisted upon their drinking before he drank.
It was from the well of Bethlehem; and David would not drink at all, but "poured it out unto Jehovah."

69. When Sisera was fleeing from Saul, he was made safe in the tent of Jezebel.
When Sisera was fleeing from Barak, he sought refuge in the tent of Jael, who killed him by driving a tent pin through his temples as he slept.

70. Leah, who had six sons, was first in Jacob's affection, because Rachel had no children.
Rachel, who was the mother of Joseph and Benjamin, was Jacob's first and greatest love.

14

II. What Verse Is Intended?

BELOW ARE GIVEN a number of paraphrases of well-known Bible verses. What verse is referred to in each paraphrase? The verse called for follows in italics.

1. The Bible says to respect your mother and dad.
"Honor thy father and thy mother."
2. Jesus said that we should always be confronted with poverty.
"Ye have the poor with you always."
3. Jesus said that discipleship involves self-denial and cross-bearing.
"If any man will come after me, let him deny himself, and take up his cross daily, and follow me."
4. Adam "passed the buck" to Eve.
"The woman whom thou gavest to be with me, she gave me of the tree, and I did eat."
5. The women of Israel made Saul jealous by singing of the superiority of David as a warrior.
"Saul hath slain his thousands, and David his ten thousands."
6. The blessing which God gave to Moses to pass on to Israel called upon God to "bless," "keep," "shine," "lift," and "give." Give the benediction.
"The Lord bless thee, and keep thee: the Lord make his face to shine upon thee, and be gracious unto thee: the Lord lift up his countenance upon thee, and give thee peace."
7. Jesus suggested that in some cases we can separate our civil duties from our religious duties.
"Render to Caesar the things that are Caesar's and to God the things that are God's."

15

III. Choose an Answer

SEVERAL ANSWERS are given for each of the following questions. Which is correct? The correct answer is given in italics.

1. In which Gospel is it recorded that Jesus was laid in a manger: Mark, *Luke,* or John?

2. Which did Noah build: a temple, a tabernacle, or *an ark?*

3. Who was the first Christian martyr: James, *Stephen,* or Paul?

4. Who was Isaac's wife: Rachel, Sarah, or *Rebekah?*

5. What book of the Bible contains the words, "Blessed is he that readeth": Matthew, Proverbs, or *Revelation?*

6. Which did Jacob build in Bethel: a ladder, a temple, or *an altar?*

7. David said in Psalms: "The . . . . shall be turned into hell." Which is the missing word: drunkards, *wicked,* or gluttons?

8. In which book is this passage found, "Remember now thy Creator in the days of thy youth": Song of Solomon, Proverbs, *Ecclesiastes?*

9. Who baptized the Ethiopian eunuch: Peter, *Philip,* or Paul?

10. Who slew "both a lion and a bear": Samson, Daniel, or *David?*

11. Whose wife was turned to a pillar of salt: Abraham, *Lot,* or Moses?

12. Who was the author of the Book of Lamentations: *Jeremiah,* Solomon, or David?

18

13. Who was the queen of King Agrippa: Eunice, *Bernice*, or Priscilla?

14. One daughter-in-law of Naomi's was Ruth. Who was the other: Delilah, *Orpah*, or Dorcas?

15. What is the number of Psalms in the Bible: 100, *150*, or 200?

16. Were six hundred Philistines slain by: *an ox goad*, a sword of Gideon, or the sling and stone of David?

17. "Without .... no man shall see the Lord." What is the missing word: righteousness, *holiness*, or repentance?

18. Whom did King Herod have killed with the sword: *John*, Peter, or Stephen?

19. Who said, "When I blow with a trumpet then blow ye the trumpets": Joshua, Moses, *Gideon?*

20. At whose house were "many gathered together praying": *Mary's*, Lydia's, or Hannah's?

21. Who was "a gatherer of sycamore fruit": Zaccheus, Hosea, or *Amos?*

22. Which Gospel contains these words, "Thou shalt call his name Jesus": *Matthew*, Mark, or Luke?

23. Who was the youngest son of Jacob: Joseph, *Benjamin*, or Ephraim?

24. Who wrote First Timothy: Timothy, *Paul*, or Matthew?

25. Who in the New Testament "used sorcery and bewitched the people": *Simon*, Alexander, or Ananias?

26. Who took refuge in the Cave of Adullam: Samson, *David*, or Joseph?

27. How many "cities of refuge" were to be appointed (in the Book of Numbers): *6*, 7, or 12?

28. Elijah was commanded to hide by what brook: *Cherith*, Kidron, or Jordan?

29. Who was the father of John the Baptist: Simon, *Zacharias*, or Zechariah?

30. Which of these books does not contain the word "God": *Esther*, Ecclesiastes, or James?

31. Who gave the Golden Rule: Moses, John, or *Jesus?*

32. Who was David's great friend: Saul, *Jonathan,* or Solomon?

33. Where was Jesus born: in Nazareth, in Jerusalem, or *in Bethlehem?*

34. Which book of the Bible means "beginning": Matthew, *Genesis,* or Deuteronomy?

35. Who was the disciple chosen to take the place of Judas: Paul, Justus, or *Matthias?*

36. Name two boys whose coats were especially mentioned in the Bible: *Samuel*, Abel, *Joseph*, David.

37. When the wise men came to the infant Jesus, what did they bring: gifts of *gold,* precious stones, *myrrh, frankincense,* or food?

38. How does the Beatitude "Blessed are the pure in heart" end: "for they shall be called great," "for they shall inherit the earth," or *"for they shall see God"?*

39. Who was the first boy of Bible history: Adam, *Cain,* Samuel, or David?

40. Where was Samuel's home: in Jerusalem, *in Ramah,* or in Egypt?

41. Who helped Jesus bear his cross: *Simon,* Joseph of Arimathea, or Pilate?

42. Where is the parable of the good Samaritan found: in the Gospel of John, *in the Gospel of Luke,* in Psalms, or in Deuteronomy?

43. Who spoke the text, "Inasmuch as ye have done it unto one of the least of these my brethren, ye have done it unto me": Paul, *Jesus,* or John the Baptist?

44. Who said, "I will arise and go to my father": Peter, *the prodigal son,* or Paul?

45. Which was the chief city of Palestine during Jesus' day: Jericho, Bethlehem, *Jerusalem,* or Capernaum?

46. What man had a daughter who was raised to life: Nicodemus, Joseph, or *Jairus?*

47. Of what tribe was Jesus a member: Levi, *Judah*, Benjamin, or Dan?

48. By whom was Simon Peter brought to Jesus: John, *Andrew*, James, or Philip?

49. What does the name "Peter" mean: rough, ready, *rock*, or reliable?

50. Among the following, which three witnessed the transfiguration of Jesus: *James*, Andrew, *Peter*, Matthew, *John*, Judas?

IV. True or False?

DECIDE whether the following statements are true or false. If false, correct them. Correct answers follow in italics.

1. Noah's Ark was made of steel. *False; it was made of gopher wood.*

2. In the beginning, Abraham created the heaven and the earth. *False; God was the creator.*

3. It is said of David that he slew more men in his death than he did in his life. *False; this was true of Samson.*

4. Noah was the name of a daughter of Zelophehad. *True.*

5. Phinehas was the son of Hopni. *False; the two were brothers.*

6. Manasseh is spoken of as a "cake not turned." *False; this statement was made concerning his brother Ephraim.*

7. Mahlon and Chilion were the husbands of Ruth and Orpha. *True.*

8. Jacob had twelve sons, but no daughters. *False; Dinah was a daughter of Jacob.*

9. Chedorlaomer was once King of Elam. *True.*

10. Joshua and Caleb were brothers. *False; they were associates in spying on the land of Canaan.*

11. Tabitha and Dorcas were sisters. *False; these were two names for the same woman.*

12. Jesus had to bear the cross all the way to Calvary. *False; Simon helped him.*

13. Jesus was rejected in his home town of Nazareth. *True.*

14. John the Baptist was one of the twelve disciples. *False; he was the "forerunner" of the Christ.*

22

15. Man was made for the Sabbath. *False; the Sabbath was made for man.*

16. John the Baptist wrote the Gospel according to John. *False; it was the Apostle John.*

17. Peter once paid both his and Jesus' taxes with money from a fish's mouth. *True.*

18. Peter was known as the disciple whom Jesus loved. *False; it was John.*

19. "Blessed are the peacemakers, for theirs is the kingdom of heaven." *False; ". . . for they shall be called the children of God."*

20. "Blessed are the troublemakers, for they shall be called the children of God." *False; "Blessed are the peacemakers. . . ."*

21. James was known as "the doubting disciple." *False; it was Thomas.*

22. Jesus' active ministry lasted three years. *True.*

23. Lazarus climbed into a tree to see Jesus. *False; it was Zacchaeus.*

24. Lot looked back after leaving Sodom. *False; it was Lot's wife.*

25. To see if water was receding, Noah sent out a dove. *True.*

26. Paul visited Greece and preached in Athens. *True.*

27. Barnabas was the first Christian martyr. *False; it was Stephen.*

28. Saul gave his consent to the murder of Stephen. *True.*

29. The Sanhedrin was a Jewish temple. *False; it was a court.*

30. The disciple who denied that he knew Christ afterward suffered persecution for preaching Christ's gospel. *True; it was Peter.*

31. Paul raised Lazarus from the dead. *False; Jesus did.*

32. Peter, James, and John were with Jesus on the Mount of Transfiguration. *True.*

23

33. The Book of Revelation was written by James. *False; it was written by John.*

34. Timothy wrote the Epistles bearing his name. *False; it was Paul.*

35. Peter washed the feet of the apostles at the Last Supper. *False; Jesus did.*

36. Pilate said that Jesus ought to be crucified because he claimed to be King of the Jews. *False; Pilate found no fault with him for this.*

37. The good Samaritan was a friend to the man who fell among thieves. *True.*

38. Roman soldiers crucified Jesus between two thieves. *True.*

39. Peter bravely defended Jesus at his trial before Pilate. *False; he denied him.*

40. Judas pretended to love Jesus, but showed by his acts that he loved money more. *True.*

41. The Beatitudes and the Lord's Prayer are parts of the Sermon on the Mount. *True.*

42. While Jesus was fasting and being tempted in the wilderness, his twelve disciples awaited his return in Jerusalem. *False; he had no disciples then.*

43. John the Baptist asked that he might be baptized by Jesus. *True.*

44. Mary and Joseph lived in Egypt until Herod died. *True.*

45. Herod asked the wise men to tell him when they found Jesus in order that he might worship him. *True; but Herod's reason was false.*

46. Jesus was born in Jerusalem. *False; he was born in Bethlehem.*

47. Adam and Eve were driven from Eden because they disobeyed God. *True.*

48. During the absence of Moses, the children of Israel

made a serpent of brass for an idol. *False; they made a golden calf.*

49. Moses led the children of Israel into the Promised Land of Canaan. *False; Joshua did.*

50. Aaron was called "the great lawgiver." *False; Moses was called that.*

51. Nehemiah refused to rebuild the walls of Jerusalem. *False; he rebuilt them.*

52. Isaiah was the prophet of lamentations. *False; it was Jeremiah.*

53. Elijah won a victory over the priests of Baal on Mount Carmel. *True.*

54. Esther was a Jewish maiden who married a king of Persia. *True.*

55. Daniel disobeyed the King's commandment in order to worship God according to his usual custom. *True.*

56. Joshua was the leader of the Israelites after the death of Moses. *True.*

57. Joseph was put in prison because he told the King there was going to be famine. *False; Potiphar's wife was responsible.*

58. As a boy, Joseph was sold by his own brothers and taken to Egypt. *True.*

59. Abraham was unselfish and allowed his nephew to choose the best land. *True.*

60. The twelve spies sent into Canaan reported that the people were friendly. *False; none of them did.*

61. Samson killed Goliath. *False; David did.*

62. Jonathan saved David's life. *True.*

63. David was the first King of Israel. *False; Saul was.*

64. Ruth was the sister of Naomi. *False; Ruth was Naomi's daughter-in-law.*

65. Absalom was treacherous and proud, and he tried to become king. *True.*

66. Jesus could see little worth in Peter. *False; Jesus saw great possibilities in him.*

67. Peter was an impetuous man. *True.*

68. Jesus charged his disciples to tell all that he was the Christ. *False—during part of his ministry.*

69. Jesus told Peter that he would deny Jesus as soon as he heard the cock crow. *False; Jesus told Peter he would have denied Jesus three times before he heard the cock crow.*

70. Joseph went to Bethlehem to be taxed because he belonged to the tribe of Benjamin, who had once lived at Bethlehem. *False; Joseph was of David's house.*

71. Only one angel delivered to the shepherds the news of the birth of Jesus. *True.*

72. A star in the east guided the shepherds to the manger in which the baby Jesus lay. *False; the wise men were thus guided.*

73. The Scriptures do not tell how many wise men came from the east to see the baby Jesus. *True; legend is responsible for the idea that there were three.*

74. The Scriptures say that the wise men rode on camels. *False; the Scriptures do not mention the camels.*

75. The wise men told Joseph to take the baby Jesus into Egypt to escape the wrath of Herod. *False; an angel did.*

76. The wise men did not meet the shepherds at the manger in which Jesus lay. *True.*

77. Joseph was told by an angel of the Lord that the name of the Savior should be Jesus. *True.*

78. The soldiers broke the legs of Jesus and the two thieves before removing them from the cross. *False; they broke the legs of the thieves, but not of Jesus. They pierced his side.*

79. In answer to Pilate, Jesus said that he was born to be a king. *True.*

80. Jesus said that God could not forgive us our trespasses unless we forgave others. *True.*

81. Jesus once healed ten lepers, and all but one returned to thank him. *False; only one returned.*

82. Jesus once cooked a breakfast of fish for his disciples. *True.*

83. Jesus said: "Thou shalt love thy neighbor and hate thine enemy." *False; he said: ". . . love thine enemy."*

84. Jesus received no schooling. *False; all Jewish boys attended the synagogue school.*

85. Thomas betrayed Jesus with a kiss. *False; it was Judas.*

86. Jesus said to Peter: "Yet lackest thou one thing." *False; he said this to the rich young ruler.*

87. Judas lived to enjoy the money he received for betraying Christ. *False; he committed suicide.*

88. Jesus did not eat with sinners for fear of setting a bad example. *False; Jesus ate with sinners. He came to save them.*

89. Jesus always gave thanks before he ate. *True.*

90. When his life was in danger, Jesus sometimes had to withdraw from public sight. *True.*

91. John the Baptist was accused of having a devil because he ate bread and drank wine. *False; John the Baptist neither ate bread nor drank wine.*

92. The Devil quoted Scripture when he was tempting Jesus to sin. *True.*

93. Jesus' brothers were his loyal followers during his earthly ministry. *False; it was not until after the resurrection.*

94. The relative size of Palestine is that of the state of Texas. *False; Palestine is about the size of New Jersey or New Hampshire.*

95. The Gospel of John is the third book of the New Testament. *False; it is the fourth book.*

96. Jesus' suffering was so great on the cross that he forgot all about his mother. *False; he asked John to care for her.*

97. Jesus and his disciples were often so busy doing good that they had no leisure even to eat. *True.*

98. Jesus said no one could enter the kingdom unless his righteousness exceeded that of the good Samaritan. *False; he said not unless he exceed the righteousness of the scribes and Pharisees.*

99. Jesus' mother was present when his first recorded miracle was performed. *True; it was at the wedding at Cana.*

100. Peter won his race with John to the tomb of the Lord. *False; John won the race, but Peter was the first to enter the tomb.*

101. Jesus raised Peter's mother-in-law from the dead. *False; he healed her fever.*

102. After his resurrection, Jesus came through a shut door to his disciples. *True.*

103. Jesus said: "Whosoever shall smite thee on thy right cheek, be sure to smite him back." *False; he said: ". . . turn to him the other also."*

104. Jesus both asked and answered questions in the temple at the age of twelve. *True.*

105. Jesus once said that false Christs would rise up and do great wonders to deceive God's people. *True.*

106. Jesus was the youngest child in the family. *False; he was the oldest of at least seven children.*

107. Peter was one disciple who was always faithful to Christ. *False; he fought for Christ, yet denied him.*

108. Jesus compared the growth of a mustard seed to the growth of a child. *False; he compared it to the growth of the kingdom of heaven.*

109. Jesus once said that the people in the next world will be married as they are now. *False; see Mark 12:25.*

110. Jesus and his disciples sang a hymn just before they went to the Garden of Gethsemane. *True.*

111. Jesus once healed a dumb man, who went out and

brought in two blind men to be given sight. *False; the blind men to whom Jesus had given sight brought in the dumb man.*

112. Rachel was Leah's sister. *True.*

113. Benjamin and Gideon were brothers. *False; both were descended from Jacob, however.*

114. Dinah and Leah were sisters. *False; Leah was Dinah's mother.*

115. Simeon and Samuel were brothers. *False; they were not related.*

116. Hannah was Eli's wife. *False; Hannah's husband was named Elkanah.*

117. Saul was Jonathan's father. *True.*

118. Deborah was Barak's sister. *False; Deborah was a judge, and Barak led the army for her.*

119. Hophni and Phinehas were brothers. *True.*

120. Joseph and Zebulun were brothers. *True; they were half-brothers.*

121. Jacob sold his birthright to his brother Esau for a mess of pottage. *False; it was just the reverse.*

122. Jesus was born in Nazareth. *False; it was in Bethlehem.*

123. Jesus turned water into wine at a wedding feast in Capernaum. *False; it was at Cana.*

124. Jesus called Matthew to be his follower while they were fishing. *False; he did so as Matthew was collecting taxes.*

125. Cain was killed by his brother Abel. *False; it was the other way round.*

126. Peter was called "the beloved disciple." *False; John was.*

127. Paul's sight was restored in the home of a man named Judas. *True.*

128. The Trinity refers to Mary, Joseph, and Jesus. *False; it refers to God, Christ, and the Holy Spirit.*

29

129. No miracles were performed until Jesus came. *False; the Old Testament reports many miracles.*

130. Gethsemane was the village where Mary and Martha lived. *False; they lived at Bethany. Gethsemane was the garden where Jesus prayed the night of his arrest.*

131. Esther wrote the story of her life while in prison. *False; the author of Esther is unknown.*

132. The King James version of the Bible is no longer in use. *False; it is the best-known version of the Bible.*

133. Jesus said: "How far that little candle throws his beams; so shines a good deed in a naughty world." *False; Portia said it in Shakespeare's* Merchant of Venice.

134. The Gospel of Matthew is the first book of the New Testament. *True.*

135. There are thirteen history books in the New Testament. *False; there is but one, the Book of Acts.*

136. One of the twelve apostles was called Didymus. *True; Thomas was so called.*

137. Elephants are not mentioned in the Bible; hence we can assume that elephants were unknown to the people of that era. *False; ivory was widely used, being mentioned several times.*

138. "The Lord tempers the wind to the shorn lamb" is quoted from Proverbs. *False; the quotation comes from* A Sentimental Journey, *by Laurence Sterne.*

139. Nebuchadnezzar saw three men in the fiery furnace. *False; he saw four.*

140. Shadrach, Meshach, and Abednego were the real names of those cast into the furnace. *False; Hananiah, Mishael, and Azariah were their Hebrew names.*

141. Confucius (born 551 B.C.) was a contemporary of Moses. *False; Moses was born about a thousand years earlier.*

142. Adam and Eve fell because they ate the forbidden apple. *False; there is no mention of an apple.*

30

143. Although they may tell the same story, no chapters of the Bible are exactly alike. *False; II Kings 19 and Isaiah 37 are alike.*

144. Belteshazzar was the name given Daniel when he was at the court of Nebuchadnezzar. *True.*

145. Jesus once picked ears of grain on the Sabbath day in order to obtain food. *False; his disciples did, but he defended them.*

146. The poor widow cast into the treasury one mite and was commended by Jesus. *False; it was two mites.*

147. John the Baptist did not drink wine. *True.*

148. The word "apostle" means ambassador in the Greek language. *True.*

149. There is no such book as Ecclesiasticus. *False; it is in the Apocrypha.*

150. Sidon was a town in Egypt. *False; it was in Phoenicia.*

V. Women of the Bible

THIS TEST covers fifty women mentioned in the Bible, some of whom were unnamed but most of whom were important, either because of their own acts or because of their relationship to a prominent character in the Bible. Of the four names given after each statement, choose the one that will make the statement true. Correct answers are given in italics.

1. The mother of Cain and Abel was: Elizabeth, Esther, *Eve,* Eunice.

2. The mother of the Hebrew race was: Eve, *Sarah,* Rebekah, Leah.

3. The mother of Ishmael, Abraham's firstborn son, was: Hannah, Huldah, Herodias, *Hagar.*

4. The woman who was turned into a pillar of salt because she looked back when Sodom and Gomorrah were being destroyed was: Abraham's wife, Pilate's wife, *Lot's wife,* Ahab's wife.

5. The wife of Isaac, and the mother of Jacob and Esau, was Rachel, Rahab, Rhoda, *Rebekah.*

6. The mother of six of Jacob's twelve sons was: *Leah,* Bilhah, Rachel, Zilpah.

7. The mother of Joseph and Benjamin, for whom Jacob served Laban fourteen years, was: Zilpah, *Rachel,* Balhah, Leah.

8. The mother of Moses and Aaron was: *Jochebed,* Jael, Joanna, Jezebel.

9. The baby Moses was found in the bulrushes by: Jephthah's daughter, Jairus' daughter, a daughter of Zion, *Pharaoh's daughter.*

10. The sister of Moses and Aaron who led the children in a song of rejoicing after crossing the Red Sea was: Mary, *Miriam*, Martha, Mara.

11. The name of the "mother in Israel," who was one of the judges in a time of national disunion was: Dinah, *Deborah*, Delilah, Drusilla.

12. Sisera, the general who was routed by Deborah and Barak, was killed by: Jezebel, Joanne, *Jael*, Jochebed.

13. The young woman who was sacrificed because of a promise made before a battle was: Pharaoh's daughter, a daughter of Zion, Jairus' daughter, *Jephthah's daughter*.

14. The Philistine woman who betrayed Samson was: Drusilla, *Delilah*, Deborah, Dinah.

15. The story of a Moabitess who became the ancestress of King David is told in the Book of: Esther, Judith, *Ruth*, Suzanna.

16. The wife of Elimelech, who lived in the land of Moab because of a famine in Canaan (until the death of her husband and her two sons), was: Salome, *Naomi*, Huldah, Anna.

17. The name of Naomi's daughter-in-law who left her to return to her own people was: Ruth, Esther, Rhoda, *Orpah*.

18. The words, "Entreat me not to leave thee, and to return from following after thee," were spoken by: Naomi, *Ruth*, Orpah, Rebekah.

19. The mother of Samuel, the greatest seer in the history of Israel, was: Huldah, Hagar, Herodias, *Hannah*.

20. The younger daughter of King Saul who became David's wife was: Maachah, *Michal*, Mahalath, Merab.

21. The discreet woman who became the wife of Jacob after the death of her husband Nabal was: *Abigail*, Bathsheba, Michal, Ahinoam.

22. The mother of Solomon was: Ahinoam, Michal, *Bathsheba*, Abigail.

23. The famous woman who came from another country

because she had heard of the wisdom of Solomon was: Diana of the Ephesians, a Samaritan woman, the Shunemite, *the Queen of Sheba*.

24. The wife of King Ahab, who caused a Hebrew to be slain for the sake of a vineyard that her husband wanted to own, was: Esther, *Jezebel*, Herodias, Bernice.

25. The girl who persuaded Naaman, the Syrian, to follow the instructions of Elisha in order to be healed of leprosy was: A daughter of Jerusalem, a slave girl of Philippi, *a captive maid*, the daughter of a Syrophoenician woman.

26. The name of a Hebrew prophetess in the time of King Josiah was: Hannah, Herodias, Hagar, *Huldah*.

27. The story of a beautiful Jewess who married a Persian king is told in the Book of: Suzanna, Ruth, Judith, *Esther*.

28. The unfaithful wife who became the symbol of God's loving forgiveness of Israel was: *Gomer*, Orpah, Dorcas, Lydia.

29. The mother of Jesus was: Elizabeth, Martha, *Mary*, Sarah.

30. The mother of John the Baptist was: Sarah, Mary, Martha, *Elizabeth*.

31. The Jewess prophetess "of a great age" who gave thanks to God when she saw the infant Jesus in the temple was: *Anna*, Sapphira, Deborah, Huldah.

32. The woman who lay sick of a fever and ministered to Jesus and his disciples after he had healed her was: the widow of Nain, *Simon's wife's mother*, the woman at the well, the widow who cast two mites into the treasury.

33. The twelve-year old girl who lived near the Sea of Galilee whom Jesus restored to health was: the daughter of Herodias, a daughter of Jerusalem, *Jairus' daughter*, the daughter of a Syrophoenician woman.

34. The wife of the tetrarch who asked for the head of John the Baptist on a charger was: Bernice, *Herodias*, Jezebel, Esther.

35. The woman of great faith who urged Jesus to heal her daughter even though she was of a different race was: the Samaritan woman, the widow of Nain, the *Syrophoenician woman*, a woman of Thyatira.

36. The young woman who was troubled with much serving was: Mary, Tabitha, *Martha*, Salome.

37. The woman of Bethany who appreciated Jesus' spiritual message was: Salome, Martha, Tabitha, *Mary*.

38. The social outcast who was converted by Jesus and became one of his faithful followers, and to whom he revealed himself in the garden of Joseph of Arimathea, was: the Samaritan woman, *Mary Magdalene*, Gomer, the slave girl of Philippi.

39. The mother of James and John, who was present at the crucifixion of Jesus and later visited his sepulchre, was: Mary, *Salome*, Mara, Naomi.

40. The mother of John Mark, whose home was a meeting place for the followers of Jesus, was: Priscilla, Eunice, *Mary*, Lois.

41. The member of the early Christian community who loved her property more than she loved her fellow members was: Priscilla, Tabitha, *Sapphira*, Anna.

42. The maid in the home of the mother of John Mark who left Peter standing at the gate while she ran and told the company praying in the house that he was released from prison was: *Rhoda*, Phoebe, Lois, Eunice.

43. The woman full of good works who was restored to health by Peter was: Rhoda, Priscilla, *Lydia*, Dorcas.

44. The seller of purple, a woman of Thyatira, who became one of Paul's converts, was: *Dorcas*, Lydia, Priscilla, Rhoda.

45. The wife of Aquila, in whose home Paul stayed while he was in Corinth because he was of the same trade as he was: Drusilla, *Priscilla*, Eunice, Bernice.

46. The wife of Felix, Governor of Judea, was: Eunice, Bernice, Priscilla, *Drusilla*.

47. The sister of King Agrippa was: Herodias, *Bernice*, Phoebe, Lois.

48. The deaconess who was the bearer of the Epistle to the Romans was: Lydia, Dorcas, Priscilla, *Phoebe*.

49. The grandmother of a beloved fellow worker of Paul was: *Lois*, Huldah, Eunice, Anna.

50. The mother of Timothy was: Anna, *Eunice*, Huldah, Lois.

VI. Bible Relatives

Establish the following relationships. Correct answers follow in italics.

A. Brothers:

1. Who were the first brothers? *Cain and Abel.*
2. Name three sons of Noah. *Ham, Shem, Japheth.*
3. What two half-brothers were sons of Abraham? *Ishmael and Isaac.*
4. Name twin brothers who were sons of Isaac. *Esau and Jacob.*
5. Name six sons of Jacob and Leah. *Reuben, Simeon, Levi, Judah, Issachar, and Zebulun.*
6. Name the two sons of Jacob and Rachel. *Joseph and Benjamin.*
7. What two brothers were the sons of Joseph and his Egyptian wife? *Ephraim and Manasseh.*
8. Name the leader who led the Israelites out of Egypt and his brother who became their first high priest. *Moses and Aaron.*
9. One of David's sons attempted to seize his father's throne; another inherited the throne. Who were these half-brothers? *Absalom and Solomon.*
10. Name four brothers of Jesus. *James, Joseph, Simon, and Judas.*
11. Name one of the early disciples and the brother he brought to Jesus. *Andrew and Peter.*
12. Name the brothers who were fishermen with their father Zebedee. *James and John.*

B. Sisters:

1. What sister watched over her hidden baby brother? *Miriam*.

2. Name two sisters who were wives of the same man. *Leah and Rachel*.

3. Name the sisters-in-law who married the sons of Naomi. *Ruth and Orpah*.

4. What man had three daughters and seven sons? *Job*.

5. Who was the sister of Jacob's twelve sons? *Dinah*.

6. What two sisters were among the most loved friends of Jesus? *Martha and Mary*.

7. What are the names of the sisters of Jesus? *We do not know*.

8. Whose sister was Tamar? *Absalom's*.

C. Husbands and Wives:

1. What husband and wife had no parents? *Adam and Eve*.

2. Name the husband and wife who left home and people to travel to a promised land. *Abram and Sarai*.

3. Eliezer was sent to a far land to find a bride for his master's son. Who were the bride and groom? *Rebekah and Isaac*.

4. Who was the wife of her cousin through her father's deception, and who was her husband? *Leah and Jacob*.

5. Who was the husband who gave fourteen years of service for his wife, and who was the wife? *Jacob and Rachel*.

6. What husband and wife first met in a harvest field? *Boaz and Ruth*.

7. A churlish farmer was saved from death by his diplomatic wife when he rudely refused to give aid to one in need. After his death by illness, his widow married the man whom her husband had offended. Who were the farmer and his

wife; and who was the second husband, later a great king? *Nabal and Abigail; David.*

8. A powerful king desired the wife of a soldier; so he had him killed in battle in order that the wife might be free to marry. Who were the soldier and his wife, and who was the king? *Uriah and Bathsheba; David.*

9. Who was the most wicked queen in the Bible, and who was her husband? *Jezebel and Ahab.*

10. What beautiful wife risked her own life to save her people; and who was her husband, a powerful king? *Esther and Ahasuerus.*

11. What mother has been most revered in the world, and who was her husband? *Mary and Joseph.*

12. Who were the parents of John the Baptist? *Zacharias and Elizabeth.*

13. What husband and wife were struck dead for lying? *Ananias and Sapphira.*

14. What husband and wife shared their home with Paul and aided in Christian work? *Aquilla and Priscilla.*

15. Who was the wife of Elimelech? *Naomi.*

VII. Bible Associations

WHAT BIBLE CHARACTER do you think of in connection with the following phrases? Correct answers are given in italics.

1. A beautiful garden. *Adam and Eve.*
2. Thirty pieces of silver. *Judas.*
3. A large boat. *Noah.*
4. Three denials of Jesus. *Peter.*
5. The golden wedge. *Achan.*
6. A tent pin. *Jael or Sisera.*
7. A burning bush. *Moses.*
8. The golden calf. *Aaron.*
9. A pot of oil. *Elisha.*
10. Boils. *Job.*
11. The scarlet cord. *Rahab or the two spies.*
12. A slingshot. *David or Goliath.*
13. A coat of many colors. *Joseph.*
14. A pillar of salt. *Lot's wife.*
15. The left-handed man. *Ehud.*
16. The fleece. *Gideon.*
17. The strong man. *Samson.*
18. The tall king. *Saul.*
19. The great friendship. *David and Jonathan.*
20. The wicked queen. *Jezebel.*
21. The bald-headed man. *Elisha.*
22. The weeping prophet. *Jeremiah.*
23. The valley of dry bones. *Ezekiel.*
24. The lion's den. *Daniel.*
25. A manger. *The infant Jesus.*
26. The doubter. *Thomas.*
27. The martyr. *Stephen.*
28. The forerunner. *John the Baptist.*
29. The three hundred. *Gideon.*
30. The Feast of Purim. *The Book of Esther.*

VIII. The Bible in Figures

THE ANSWERS to the following questions are in numeral form. Correct answers are given in italics.

A. A Page from the Book of Numbers:

1. At the time of the flood, how many days did it rain: 7, *40*, 20?

2. How many spies were sent into the Promised Land by Moses: *12*, 40, 10?

3. How many days were these spies in the Promised Land: 30, 70, *40?*

4. How many years did the Israelites wander in the wilderness: *40*, 70, 7?

5. How old was Noah when he died: 800, 988, *950?*

6. How many years did Jacob have to serve for each of his wives: 14, 7, 10?

7. For how many years was Nebuchadnezzar insane: 14, 7, *10?*

8. For about how many years were the Jews in captivity in Babylon: 40, 70, 7, *50?*

9. Anak was the father of how many giants: 1, 5, *3*, 2?

10. How many chapters are there in the entire Bible: 2,000, *1,189*, 500?

11. How many chapters are there in the Old Testament: *929*, 500, 1,000?

12. How many chapters are there in the New Testament: 500, 350, *260?*

13. How many times did Peter deny Christ: 1, *3*, 4?

14. How old was Jesus when he was crucified: 30, *33*, 35?

15. How old was Methuselah when he died: 900, 950, *969?*

16. How many books are there in the Protestant Bible: 56, 76, *66?*

17. How many books are there in the New Testament: *27*, 39, 29, 37?

18. How old was Jesus when he was taken to the Feast of the Passover: 10, *12*, 14?

19. How many days did Moses stay in the mountains talking to God: 21, 30, *40?*

20. Of the ten lepers that Jesus healed, how many came back and thanked him: 9, 0, 3, *1?*

21. How many Philistines did Shamgar, a judge of Israel, slay with an ox goad: 70, *600*, 100?

22. How many stripes did the Jews administer to criminals as a punishment: 12, *40*, 10? (See Deuteronomy 25:3.)

23. How many priests did Doeg kill: *85*, 50, 100?

24. How many disciples were sent out to teach: 10, 30, *70?*

25. How many books are in the Old Testament: 27, *39*, 29, 37?

26. How many temptations did Satan put before Jesus in the wilderness: 1, 7, 2, *3?*

27. How many thieves were crucified with Jesus: *2*, 3, 5.

28. How many brothers did Joseph have: 1, *11*, 13?

29. How many times was the leper Naaman dipped into the Jordan before he became clean: 2, *7*, 14?

30. How many disciples did Jesus have: *12*, 10, 50?

31. How many commandments was Moses given: *10*, 7, 40?

32. How many virgins took their lamps and went forth to meet the bridegroom? 5, *10*, 15?

33. How many spies were sent by Moses to spy in the Promised Land: 7, *12*, 34?

34. How many Philistines did Samson slay with the jawbone of an ass: 6, *1,000*, 5,000?

35. To how many foxes' tails did Samson tie firebrands: *300*, 3,000, 30?

36. How many of Daniel's friends were cast into the fiery furnace because they would not worship the golden image set up by King Nebuchadnezzar: 1, 3, 7?

37. How many years did Paul live as a prisoner in his own rented home in Rome: 2, 4, 6?

38. How many times did Jesus ask Peter if he loved him: 3, 6, 2?

39. How many men swore not to eat or drink until they had killed Paul: 6, 40, 100?

40. How old was Jesus when he began his ministry: 20, 21, 30?

B. Biblical Statistics:

1. How many times was Jesus tempted? 3.

2. What was Jesus' age when he said: "I must be in my Father's house"? 12 years.

3. What was the length of Paul's stay at Malta? 3 months.

4. How many colors had Joseph's coat? Many.

5. How long was Jesus on earth after his resurrection? 40 days.

6. How many apostles were with Jesus on the Mount of Transfiguration? 3.

7. How many pebbles did David pick out of the brook to slay the giant, and how many did he use? 5 and 1.

8. How many sons had Jacob? 12.

9. What is the distance from Nazareth to Jerusalem? About 70 miles.

10. How many times did the children of Israel march around Jericho? 13.

11. How many years did Jacob serve to obtain Rachel for his wife? 14.

12. How many mansions are there in our heavenly Father's house? Many.

13. The harvest truly is plenteous, but how about the laborers? Few.

43

14. Jesus said to forgive our brothers how many times? *70 times 7.*

15. Over how many sinners that repent did Jesus say there would be joy in heaven? *1.*

16. How old was Joseph, the son of Jacob, when his story opens? *17.*

17. With how many loaves and fishes did Jesus feed the five thousand? *5 loaves and 2 fishes.*

18. How many spies did Moses send to spy out the land, and how many did Joshua send? *12 and 2.*

19. How many plagues did God send on Egypt? *10.*

20. How long was Jesus on the cross? *9 hours.*

21. How many days from the Passover to Pentecost? *50.*

22. How long was Paul in Arabia after his conversion? *3 years.*

23. According to the Bible, how many proverbs did Solomon speak? *3,000.*

24. How old was Methuselah when he died? *969 years.*

25. How many times was Naaman to dip in the Jordan? *7.*

26. For how many hours did darkness cover the earth at the crucifixion of Jesus? *3.*

27. What is the number of books in the New Testament usually said to have been written by John? *5.*

28. How many disciples did Jesus send out two by two? *70.*

29. How many virgins were there in a parable told by Jesus? *10.*

30. What was the difference in years between Moses and Aaron? *3.*

31. Of those first numbered in the wilderness, how many were allowed to enter the Promised Land? *2.*

32. How many sons of Haman were hanged on the gallows? *10.*

33. What number is specified here: "Cast thy bread upon

the waters; for thou shalt find it after .... days"? *Many*.

34. What was the total number of kine that came up out of the river in Pharaoh's dream? *14*.

35. How many gates were there in the New Jerusalem, as seen in John's vision. *12*.

36. For how many years, according to Revelation, was Satan bound? *1,000*.

37. How many gold candlesticks did John see in his vision? *7*.

38. The Bible tells us that the cattle on how many hills are God's? *1,000*.

37. Peter says that one day with the Lord is as how long? *1,000 years*.

40. How many utterances did Christ make on the cross? *7*.

41. What was the greatest number of people to whom Christ made an appearance after his resurrection? *500*.

42. In what year was Solomon's temple destroyed by Nebuchadnezzar's army? *Probably 587* B.C.

43. In what year was Jerusalem destroyed by the Romans? *70* A.D.

44. What chapter of Exodus contains the Ten Commandments? *20*.

45. How many books are included in the Synoptic Gospels? *3*.

46. What is the difference between the number of pieces of silver Joseph's brothers received for selling Joseph and the number of pieces Judas received for betraying Christ? *10 (30 minus 20)*.

47. How many cities of refuge were established when the Israelites entered Canaan? *3*.

48. The tithe required that how much of one's income belongs to God? *10 per cent*.

49. Telling of his experiences in his second Corinthian letter, Paul states how many times he received how many

stripes, save how many? Therefore, how many stripes did he receive? *5 times he received 40 stripes, save 1; therefore, he received in all 195 stripes.*

50. How many were saved when the first Gospel sermon was preached by Peter? *3,000.*

C. A Problem in Bible Arithmetic:

Asked how many fish he had caught one day, a boy answered as follows:

To the number of books in the Old Testament (*39*), add the books of the New Testament (*27; total, 66*). Multiply by the number of Apostles at the Transfiguration (*3—Peter, James, and John; total, 198*). Divide by the number of books written by Luke (*2—Luke and Acts; total, 99*). Subtract the number of times the Israelites marched around Jericho (*13; total, 86*). Multiply by the number of pieces of silver Judas received for betraying Jesus (*30; total, 2,580*). Divide by the number of spies Moses sent into Canaan (*12; total, 215*). Add the number of letters in the name of the city where a man climbed a tree to see Jesus (*7—Zaccheus, at Jericho; total, 222*). Divide by the number of the apostles called the "sons of thunder" (*2—James and John; final total, 111 fish*).

IX. Bible A, B, C Tests

THE ANSWERS to the Biblical questions in Tests 1 to 6 are in alphabetical order, while those in Test 7 all begin with the letter "R." Correct answers are given in italics.

Test 1:

A. What son of David was noted for his good looks and the weight of his hair? *Absalom.*

B. What robber did the Jews choose to be released instead of Jesus when Pilate said he would release one of them? *Barabbas.*

C. What Gentile centurion was converted by the preaching of Peter, who had gone to his home, directed by a vision? *Cornelius.*

D. What Hebrew captive was put into a lion's den and remained unharmed? *Daniel.*

E. Who was the mother of John the Baptist? *Elizabeth.*

F. What was the second plague that beset the people of Egypt when they refused to allow the Israelites to go? *Frogs.*

G. In what garden did Jesus pray the night before his arrest? *Gethsemane.*

H. Who was the mother of Samuel? *Hannah.*

I. What was the name of the son that Abraham was commanded to sacrifice? *Isaac.*

J. Who was the leader of the children of Israel after the death of Moses? *Joshua.*

K. Across what brook did Jesus and the disciples go to enter the Garden of Gethsemane? *Kidron.*

L. Who was the grandmother of Timothy? *Lois.*

47

M. Where were Abraham, Isaac, and Jacob buried? *Machpelah.*

N. What captain of the host of the King of Syria was cured of leprosy by bathing in the river Jordan seven times? *Naaman.*

O. What was the name of the slave about whom Paul wrote in his letter to Philemon? *Onesimus.*

P. Who was the wife of Aquila, with whom Paul stayed at Corinth "because they were of the same craft"? *Priscilla.*

Q. In the wilderness, when the children of Israel wanted meat, what was sent them? *Quail.*

R. What Moabitess, the daughter-in-law of Naomi, was an ancestress of Jesus? *Ruth.*

S. What Assyrian king lost by a plague an army that he sent against Judea? *Sennacherib.*

T. What was Paul's home town? *Tarsus.*

U. What kind of bread was eaten at the Passover meal? *Unleavened bread.*

V. While Paul was gathering sticks to kindle a fire, after being shipwrecked on the island of Melita, what fastened itself on his hand? *A viper.*

W. Where did the children of Israel spend forty years? *In the wilderness.*

X. What Persian king stopped the rebuilding of the temple at Jerusalem? (In this answer, the clue letter does not begin the word, but is the fifth and also eighth letters in a ten-letter name.) *Artaxerxes.*

Y. What is the omitted word in this verse: "For my .... is easy, and my burden is light? *Yoke.*

Z. Who was the father of the disciples James and John? *Zebedee.*

Test 2:

A. What was the Hebrew name for Abednego? *Azariah.*

B. What king held a great feast for a thousand of his lords and drank wine before them? *Belshazzar.*

C. What Persian king allowed the Jews to rebuild the temple? *Cyrus.*

D. Who was the king who wrote psalms? *David.*

E. Who was the prophet who proved to the Israelites by fire that their God was stronger than the god of the priests of Baal? *Elijah.*

F. Who listened to Paul's case? *Felix.*

G. What is the name of the book in the Bible that deals with the history of the earth up to the time of Joseph? *Genesis.*

H. What is the name of the book in the Bible that urges the rebuilding of the temple? *Haggai.*

I. In what book is there a beautiful prophecy of the coming of the Messiah? *Isaiah.*

J. Who was the ruler who had faith that Jesus would restore his daughter to him? *Jairus.*

K. Who became Abraham's wife after the death of Sarah? *Keturah.*

L. Who was Laban's eldest daughter? *Leah.*

M. To what country was Paul called in a vision? *Macedonia.*

N. What king was so degenerated that his hairs were grown like eagle's feathers and his nails like bird's claws? *Nebuchadnezzar.*

O. On what mount did Jesus pray following the last supper? *The Mount of Olives.*

P. What was the name of Joseph's master in Egypt? *Potiphar.*

Q. When Paul was a prisoner en route to Rome, what were they afraid of when they ungirded the ship? *Quicksands.*

R. What was the name of the woman who concealed the two spies sent from Chittim? *Rahab.*

S. Before what supreme council or court was Jesus taken for trial previous to his crucifixion? *The Sanhedrin.*

T. What incident in the life of Jesus took place on a

high mountain previous to his passion? *The transfiguration.*

U. From what place did the children of Israel first migrate? *Ur of the Chaldees.*

V. What is the word used for any translation of the Bible from the original languages? *Version.*

W. For what was Solomon noted? *His wisdom.*

X. What does it take to know the Bible? *Exertion.*

Y. What was the unusual word used by Paul in Philippians in referring to a fellow laborer? *Yokefellow.*

Z. To whom did Jesus say: "Today I must abide at thy house"? *Zaccheus.*

Test 3:

A. Who was the first man? *Adam.*

B. What was the name of the tower meant to reach heaven? *Babel.*

C. What was the name of one of Adam's sons? *Cain.*

D. Who was the woman who betrayed Samson? *Delilah.*

E. Who was Adam's wife? *Eve.*

F. For how many days and nights did it rain while Noah was in the Ark? *Forty.*

G. What is the first book of the Bible? *Genesis.*

H. On what instrument did David play for King Saul? *The harp.*

I. Who was a son of Abraham? *Isaac.*

J. Who was one of Isaac's twin sons? *Jacob.*

K. What office was first filled by Saul? *That of king.*

L. Who was the man whose wife was turned to salt? *Lot.*

M. Who was the sister of Moses? *Miriam?*

N. Who was the man who built the Ark? *Noah.*

O. What is the name of one of the Old Testament books? *Obadiah.*

P. What is the name of the Old Testament book of hymns? *Psalms.*

Q. What was Ashtoreth's title when worshiped by the women of Judah? *Queen of Heaven.*

R. Who was Joseph's oldest brother? *Reuben.*

S. Who was the strongest man of Bible times? *Samson.*

T. How many did Samson slay as his last act? *3,000.*

U. Where did Job live? *In the land of Uz.*

V. What garment did Ruth wear when she gathered grain in the field of Boaz? *A veil.*

W. Who was consulted by Saul at Endor? *A witch.*

X. *X* is the ancient Greek symbol for whom? *Christ.*

Y. What is the word for "you" in the King James version of the Bible? *Ye.*

Z. Who led the Jews back from exile in 538 B.C.? *Zerubbabel.*

Test 4:

A. What man stole the golden wedge? *Achan.*

B. Who was one of Job's comforting friends? *Bildad.*

C. What was the name of the hill called "the Skull"? *Calvary.*

D. Who was the only woman judge? *Deborah.*

E. Who was the bald-headed man of the Bible? *Elisha.*

F. What are the three virtues listed in First Corinthians? *Faith, hope, and love.*

G. Which was one of the sinful cities? *Gomorrah.*

H. Who was the mother of Samuel? *Hannah.*

I. Who was the greatest Old Testament prophet? *Isaiah.*

J. What judge sacrificed his daughter? *Jephthah.*

K. What is the plural of "cow" in Genesis? *Kine.*

L. Who was the father-in-law of Jacob? *Laban.*

M. What books of the Bible contain the Beatitudes? *Matthew and Luke.*

51

N. Where was the boyhood home of Jesus? *Nazareth.*

O. What is the last letter of the Greek alphabet? *Omega.*

P. What man did Jesus call "the rock"? *Peter.*

Q. What miraculous food was found in the wilderness? *Quail.*

R. What kind of birds once fed Elijah? *Ravens.*

S. Who was the first Christian martyr? *Stephen.*

T. What disciple was called "the doubter"? *Thomas.*

U. Where was the birthplace of Abraham? *Ur.*

V. What name is given a young woman of marriageable age? *Virgin.*

W. Who were the Magi who visited Jesus? *The wise men.*

X. What was Ahasuerus' other name? *Xerxes.*

Y. What is the other name for "leaven"? *Yeast.*

Z. Who was Jethro's daughter and the wife of Moses? *Zipporah.*

Test 5:

A. What name did Eve give to her second son? *Abel.*

B. What rich man hired Ruth to glean in his fields and later married her? *Boaz.*

C. Where did Christ perform his first miracle? *Cana.*

D. Who interpreted a dream and was made a ruler in Babylon? *Daniel.*

E. Where did the baby Jesus go with his parents to escape Herod? *Egypt.*

F. What governor acquitted Paul? *Festus.*

G. At the feet of what great teacher did Paul study? *Gamaliel.*

H. Who was the mother of Ishmael? *Hagar.*

I. What was the second name of the man who betrayed Jesus? *Iscariot.*

J. Who killed Sisera? *Jael.*

K. What brook was near the Garden of Gethsemane? *Kidron.*

L. Who was called the beloved physician? *Luke.*

M. Who was the firstborn son of Joseph? *Manassah.*

N. What Syrian nobleman was healed of leprosy by bathing in the Jordan? *Naaman.*

O. Which one of Naomi's daughters-in-law returned to her own people after the death of her husband? *Orpah.*

P. What people did Samson oppose? *The Philistines.*

Q. What great queen visited Solomon and brought him gifts? *The Queen of Sheba.*

R. Which of Isaac's wives was selected by his servant? *Rebekah.*

S. Who danced before King Herod and demanded the head of John the Baptist? *Salome.*

T. What country was called the home of Saul? *Tarsus.*

U. What man did David have put in the front lines of the army because he desired the man's wife? *Uriah.*

V. What queen was dethroned because she refused to appear before King Ahasuerus? *Vashti.*

W. Where was Christ tempted by Satan? *In the wilderness.*

X. Who was a King of Persia? *Xerxes.*

Y. What did Christ say was easy to take upon oneself? *His yoke.*

Z. Which city is called the city of David? *Zion.*

Test 6:

A. Who was called "the father of the faithful"? *Abraham.*

B. Who saw a hand writing on a wall? *Belshazzar.*

C. Who was the first murderer. *Cain.*

D. Who was a harpist and writer of many psalms? *David.*

E. What high priest and judge succeeded Samuel? *Eli.*

F. What fragrant gift did the wise men bring Jesus? *Frankincense.*

G. Who was killed by a slingshot? *Goliath.*

H. Who was hanged on a gallows prepared for another? *Haman.*

I. Who was an Old Testament major prophet? *Isaiah.*

J. Who had a coat of many colors? *Joseph.*

K. Who was Saul's father. *Kish.*

L. Who was raised to life by Jesus? *Lazarus.*

M. Who was one of the Hebrew children put into the fiery furnace? *Meshach.*

N. Who owned a vineyard that Ahab coveted? *Naboth.*

O. Who was an Old Testament minor prophet? *Obadiah.*

P. Who condemned Jesus to death? *Pilate.*

Q. Who said the half had not been told of Solomon's glory? *The Queen of Sheba.*

R. Who was Jacob's favorite wife. *Rachel.*

S. Who was the first king of Israel? *Saul.*

T. Whom did Paul call his own son? *Timothy.*

U. What king had leprosy? *Uzziah.*

V. Who was a beautiful Queen of Persia? *Vashti.*

W. What name was given to Jesus by Isaiah? *Wonderful.*

X. What is another way of spelling "Christmas"? *Xmas.*

Y. When is the time to remember our Creator? *Youth.*

Z. Who climbed a tree to see Jesus. *Zaccheus.*

Test 7:

All answers begin with "R":

1. What Jewish title means "master" or "teacher"? *Rabbi.*

2. What kind of bird fed Elijah? *Raven.*

3. For what town did Syria and Israel contend? *Ramoth Gilead.*

4. What girl at a well befriended Jacob? *Rachel.*

5. Through what sea did Israel travel? *The Red Sea.*

6. What in the sky shows God's covenant? *The rainbow.*

7. Of whom was Jacob the son most prized? *Rebekah.*

8. What command is coupled with "be baptized"? *Repent.*

9. A promise of what follows "Come unto me?" *Rest.*

10. To what kind of a town could a slayer flee? *Refuge.*

11. Who saved young Joseph from the brothers' plot? *Reuben.*

12. What did Solomon say wisdom is worth more than? *Rubies.*

13. Who met Peter when he came from prison? *Rhoda.*

14. What is the meaning of Peter's name? *Rock.*

15. What "exalts a nation," giving success? *Righteousness.*

16. Who married Boaz? *Ruth.*

17. What son of Solomon saw his country divided? *Rehoboam.*

18. What book was written on the island of Patmos? *Revelation.*

19. What empire dominated Palestine in Jesus' time? *The Roman Empire.*

20. What woman protected the bones of her executed sons? *Rizpah.*

X. Bible Quotations

A. Name the book of the Bible in which the following quotations may be found:

1. "Who knoweth whether thou art come to the kingdom for such a time as this?" *Esther.*

2. "And I saw a great white throne, and him that sat on it." *Revelation.*

3. "In the beginning God created the heavens and the earth." *Genesis.*

4. "Then Agrippa said unto Paul, Almost thou persuadest me to be a Christian." *Acts.*

5. "Let there be light." *Genesis.*

6. "They shall beat their swords into plowshares, and their spears into pruning-hooks: nation shall not lift up sword against nation, neither shall they learn war any more." *Isaiah and Micah.*

7. "And the man said, The woman whom thou gavest to be with me, she gave me of the tree, and I did eat." *Genesis.*

8. "For unto us a child is born, unto us a son is given: and the government shall be upon his shoulder: and his name shall be called Wonderful, Counselor, The mighty God, The everlasting Father, The Prince of Peace." *Isaiah.*

9. "In the beginning was the Word, and the Word was with God, and the Word was God." *John.*

10. "Am I my brother's keeper?" *Genesis.*

11. "There is no new thing under the sun." *Ecclesiastes.*

12. "Sitteth in the seat of the scornful." *Psalms.*

13. "The voice is Jacob's voice, but the hands are the hands of Esau." *Genesis.*

14. "Green pastures." *Psalms.*

15. "The Lord bless thee, and keep thee: the Lord make his face shine upon thee, and be gracious unto thee: the Lord lift up his countenance upon thee, and give thee peace." *Numbers.*

16. "And now abideth faith, hope, love, these three; but the greatest of these is love." *I Corinthians.*

17. "A very present help in trouble." *Psalms.*

18. "If a man say, I love God, and hateth his brother, he is a liar." *John.*

19. "For lo, the winter is past, the rain is over and gone; the flowers appear on the earth; the time of the singing of birds is come; and the voice of the turtle-dove is heard in our land." *Song of Solomon.*

20. "I said in my haste, all men are liars." *Psalms.*

21. "I will lift up mine eyes unto the hills." *Psalms.*

22. "The Lord is in his holy temple: let all the earth keep silence before him." *Nahum.*

23. "Now there arose up a new king over Egypt, which knew not Joseph." *Exodus.*

24. "Glory to God in the highest, and on earth peace, good will toward men." *Luke.*

25. "The place whereon thou standest is holy ground." *Exodus.*

26. "Wisdom is the principal thing; therefore, get wisdom: and with all thy getting get understanding." *Proverbs.*

27. "Go to the ant, thou sluggard; consider her ways, and be wise." *Proverbs.*

28. "A false balance is an abomination to the Lord." *Proverbs.*

29. "And where thou lodgeth, I will lodge; thy people shall be my people, and thy god, my God: where thou diest, will I die, and there will I be buried." *Ruth.*

30. "A soft answer turneth away wrath." *Proverbs.*

B. What Bible character or author said or wrote these quotations?

1. "Glory to God in the highest, on earth peace." *Angels.*
2. "Behold the Lamb of God." *John the Baptist.*
3. "Depart from me, for I am a sinful man." *Peter.*
4. "Lord, if thou hadst been here my brother had not died." *Martha.*
5. "Blessed is he that cometh in the name of the Lord." *Crowds in Jerusalem.*
6. "Will ye that I release Barabbas unto you?" *Pilate.*
7. "He is not here, he is risen." *Angels.*
8. "The Lord watch between me and thee while we are absent one from the other." *Laban.*
9. "Call me Mara, for the Lord hath dealt bitterly with me." *Naomi.*
10. "Here I am, for thou didst call me." *Samuel.*
11. "Saul, Saul, why persecuteth thou me?" *Jesus.*
12. "Make haste and come down, for today I must abide at thy house." *Jesus.*
13. "What is truth?" *Pilate.*
14. "Damsel, I say unto thee, arise." *Jesus.*
15. "Behold the Lamb of God." *John the Baptist.*
16. "Thou art the Christ, the son of the living God." *Peter.*
17. "Thou are weighed in the balance and found wanting." *Daniel.*
18. "Almost thou persuadest be to be a Christian." *King Agrippa.*
19. "Take up thy bed and walk." *Jesus.*
20. "He that is without sin among you, let him first cast a stone at her." *Jesus.*
21. "Get thee behind me, Satan." *Jesus.*
22. "The place whereon thou standest is holy ground." *God.*

23. "Whatsoever thou shalt ask of me, I will give it thee, unto the half of my kingdom." *Herod.*

24. "I appeal to Caesar." *Paul.*

25. "Lord, remember me when thou comest into thy kingdom." *A thief crucified with Jesus.*

26. "Today shalt thou be with me in Paradise." *Jesus.*

27. "Joseph is not, and Simeon is not, and ye will take Benjamin away." *Jacob.*

28. "The seven good kine are seven good years." *Joseph.*

29. "Am I my brother's keeper?" *Cain.*

30. "I must be about my Father's business." *Jesus.*

31. "This is my beloved Son in whom I am well pleased." *God.*

32. "Good Master, what shall I do to inherit eternal life?" *A rich young ruler.*

33. "What shall be done unto the man whom the king delighteth to honor?" *King Ahasuerus.*

34. "Let us make man in our image." *God.*

35. "We have toiled all night and have caught nothing, nevertheless at thy word I will let down the net." *Fishermen.*

36. "Let there be light!" *God.*

37. "Behold the man!" *Pilate.*

38. "We have seen his star in the east." *Wise men.*

39. "Go ye into all the world and preach the Gospel to every creature." *Jesus.*

40. "A prophet is not without honor save in his own country and among his own people." *Jesus.*

41. "Truly this was the Son of God." *A soldier at Jesus' crucifixion.*

42. "My son, God will provide himself a lamb for a burnt offering." *Abraham.*

43. "Have nothing to do with this just man, for I have suffered many things this day in a dream because of him." *Pilate's wife.*

44. "I will not let thee go except thou bless me." *Jacob.*

59

45. "Stand up. I myself also am a man." *Peter*.

46. "If a man die, shall he live again?" *Job*.

47. "'Unto you is born this day in the city of David a savior, which is Christ the Lord." *Angels*.

48. "Where is he that is born King of the Jews?" *Wise men*.

49. "Entreat me not to leave thee or to return from following thee." *Ruth*.

50. "The voice is Jacob's voice, but the hands are the hands of Esau." *Isaac*.

51. "Let judgment run down as waters, and righteousness as a mighty stream." *Amos*.

52. "Prepare to meet thy God." *Amos*.

53. "Where wast thou when I laid the foundations of the earth?" *God*.

54. "Shall we receive good at the hand of God, and shall we not receive evil?" *Job*.

55. "If the Lord be God, then follow him; but if Baal, then follow him." *Elijah*.

56. "Go up, thou bald head." *Children*.

57. "O Absalom, my son, would God I had died for thee." *David*.

58. "Silver and gold have I none, but what I have that give I thee." *Peter*.

59. "Lord, what wilt thou have me to do?" *Paul*.

60. "If it be thy will, remove this cup from me; nevertheless not my will but thine be done." *Jesus*.

61. "Now abideth faith, hope, and love, these three; but the greatest of these is love." *Paul*.

62. "I saw a new heaven and a new earth, for the first heaven and the first earth were passed away." *John*.

63. "Who do men say that I am?" *Jesus*.

64. "Scribes and Pharisees, hypocrites." *Jesus*.

65. "Every valley shall be exalted, every mountain and hill shall be made low." *Isaiah*.

66. "Vanity of vanities! All is vanity!" *The author of Ecclesiastes.*

67. "I will go in unto the king, which is not according to the law, and if I perish, I perish." *Esther.*

68. "Who knoweth whether thou art come to the kingdom for such a time as this?" *Mordecai.*

69. "Love one another as I have loved you." *Jesus.*

70. "I will arise and go to my father." *The prodigal son.*

71. "Let me die with the Philistines." *Samson.*

72. "Saul has slain his thousands, and David his ten thousands." *Hebrew people.*

73. "Let us go even unto Bethlehem and see this thing which is come to pass." *Shepherds.*

74. "One mightier than I cometh, the lachet of whose shoes I am not worthy to unloose." *John the Baptist.*

75. "It is easier for a camel to go through a needle's eye than for a rich man to enter the kingdom of heaven." *Jesus.*

76. "Before the cock crow thou shalt deny me thrice." *Jesus.*

77. "Lazarus, come forth." *Jesus.*

78. "Unto us a child is born, unto us a son is given." *Isaiah.*

79. "In the beginning was the Word, and the Word was with God, and the Word was God." *John.*

80. "Remember the Sabbath day to keep it holy." *Moses.*

81. "O death, where is thy sting?" *Paul.*

82. "I have fought a good fight, I have finished the course, I have kept the faith." *Paul.*

83. "You must be born again." *Jesus.*

84. "Woman, behold thy son." *Jesus.*

85. "Suffer little children to come unto me and forbid them not." *Jesus.*

86. "Father, forgive them, for they know not what they do." *Jesus.*

87. "Repent! The kingdom of god is at hand." *John the Baptist.*

88. "Do this in remembrance of me." *Jesus.*

89. "Let not the sun go down upon your wrath." *Paul.*

90. "The Philistines be upon thee, Samson." *Delilah.*

91. "The woman whom thou gavest to be with me, she gave me of the tree, and I did eat." *Adam.*

92. "Art thou the King of the Jews?" *Pilate.*

93. "I was not disobedient unto the heavenly vision." *Paul.*

94. "Be strong and of a good courage; be not afraid, neither be thou dismayed. . . ." *God.*

95. "I will make of thee a great nation. . . ." *God.*

96. "Be ye doers of the word, and not hearers only . . ." *James.*

97. "The dream of Pharaoh is one: God hath showed Pharaoh what he is about to do." *Joseph.*

98. "Take this child away, and nurse it for me, and I will give thee thy wages." *Pharaoh's daughter.*

99. "All we like sheep have gone astray." *Isaiah.*

100. "Why callest thou me good? None is good, save one, that is God." *Jesus.*

C. Complete these quotations.

1. "Remember the Sabbath day: *to keep it holy.*"

2. "Let your light so shine before men, that they may see your good works: *and glorify your Father which is in heaven.*"

3. "Except ye be converted and become as little children: *ye shall not enter the kingdom of heaven.*"

4. "Where two or three are gathered together: *in my name, there am I in the midst of them.*"

5. "God is a spirit: *and they that worship him must worship him in spirit and in truth.*"

6. "Destroy this temple and in three days: *I will raise it up.*"

7. "I am come that they might have life: *and have it more abundantly.*"

8. "The Son of Man came not to be ministered unto: *but to minister, and to give his life a ransom for many.*"

9. "For what is a man profited: *if he shall gain the whole world and lose his own soul?*"

10. Though your sins be as scarlet: *they shall be white as snow.*"

11. "Seek ye the Lord while he may be found: *call ye upon him while he is near.*"

12. "Let the wicked forsake his way: *and the unrighteous man his thoughts; and let him return unto the Lord, and he shall have mercy upon him.*"

13. "Let judgment run down as waters: *and righteousness as a mighty stream.*"

14. "They shall beat their swords: *into plowshares and their spears into pruning hooks.*"

15. "Now abideth faith, hope: *love, these three; but the greatest of these is love.*"

16. "What doth the Lord require of thee: *but to do justly, and to love mercy, and to walk humbly with thy God?*"

17. "Like as a father pitieth his children: *so the Lord pitieth them that fear him.*"

18. "O that men would praise the Lord for His goodness: *and for his wonderful works to the children of men.*"

19. "From the rising of the sun until the going down of the same: *the Lord's name be praised.*"

20. "This is the day which the Lord hath made: *we will rejoice and be glad in it.*"

21. "Except the Lord build the house: *they labor in vain that build it.*"

22. "My help cometh from the Lord: *which made heaven and earth.*"

23. "Teach me, O Lord, the way of thy statutes: *and I shall keep it unto the end.*"

24. "The Lord is merciful and gracious: *slow to anger and plenteous in mercy.*"

25. "As far as the east is from the west: *so far hath he removed our transgressions from us.*"

26. "Bless the Lord, O my soul: *and all that is within me, bless his holy name.*"

27. "Enter into his gates with thanksgiving: *and into his courts with praise.*"

28. "Faith is the substance of things hoped for: *the evidence of things not seen.*"

29. "Be ye doers of the word: *and not hearers only.*"

30. "God so loved the world: *that he gave his only begotten son, that whosoever believeth in him should not perish, but have everlasting life.*"

31. "Cast thy bread upon the waters: *for thou shalt find it after many days.*"

32. "The just shall live: *by faith.*"

33. "The earth shall be filled with the knowledge of the glory of the Lord, as the: *waters cover the sea.*"

34. "The Lord is in his holy temple: *let all the earth keep silence before him.*"

35. "Let the words of my mouth and the meditation of my heart: *be acceptable in thy sight, O Lord, my strength and my redeemer.*"

36. "Lift up your heads, O ye gates: *even lift them up, ye everlasting doors, and the King of Glory shall come in.*"

37. "So teach us to number our days: *that we may apply our hearts unto wisdom.*"

38. "He that dwelleth in the secret place of the Most High: *shall abide under the shadow of the Almighty.*"

39. "O come, let us worship and bow down: *let us kneel before the Lord our maker.*"

40. "Let the people praise thee, O God: *let all the people praise thee.*"

41. "Make a joyful noise unto God: *all ye lands.*"

42. "Create in me a clean heart, O God: *and renew a right spirit within me.*"

43. "Be still and know: *that I am God.*"

44. "The Lord of Hosts is with us: *the God of Jacob is our refuge.*"

45. "God is our refuge and our strength: *a very present help in trouble.*"

46. "As the hart panteth after water brooks: *so panteth my soul after thee, O God.*"

47. "Keep thy tongue from evil: *and thy lips from speaking guile.*"

48. "The Lord is my light and my salvation: *whom shall I fear?*"

49. "The Lord is my shepherd: *I shall not want.*

50. "The earth is the Lord's and the fullness thereof: *the world and they that dwell therein.*"

51. "The heavens declare the glory of God: *and the firmament showeth his handiwork.*"

52. "Lord, who shall abide in thy tabernacle: *who shall dwell in thy holy hill?*"

53. "I was glad when they said unto me: *let us go into the house of the Lord.*"

54. "Father, forgive them: *for they know not what they do.*"

55. "Today shalt thou be with me: *in paradise.*"

56. "Woman, behold: *thy son.*"

57. "My God, my God, why: *hast thou forsaken me?*"

58. "Into thy hands: *I commend my spirit.*"

59. "Blessed are the pure in heart: *for they shall see God.*"

60. "Blessed are they that mourn: *for they shall be comforted.*"

61. "Blessed are the merciful: *for they shall obtain mercy.*"

62. "Blessed are the peacemakers: *for they shall be called the children of God.*"

63. "Blessed is the man that walketh not in the counsel of the ungodly: *nor standeth in the way of sinners, nor sitteth in the seat of the scornful.*"

64. "Yea, though I walk through the valley of the shadow of death: *I will fear no evil, for thou art with me; thy rod and thy staff they comfort me.*"

65. "Surely goodness and mercy shall follow me all the days of my life: *and I will dwell in the house of the Lord forever.*"

66. "He shall save his people from their: *sins.*"

67. "It is lawful to do .... on the Sabbath." *Good.*

68. "I am the ....; ye are the branches." *Vine.*

69. "If any man will follow me let him .... himself." *Deny.*

70. "How hardly shall they that have .... enter into the kingdom of God." *Riches.*

71. "Bless them which .... you." *Persecute.*

72. "Lo, I am with you: *always.*"

73. "Be ye .... of the word and not hearers only." *Doers.*

74. "Now abideth faith, hope: *love.*"

75. "Without .... it is impossible to please him." *Faith.*

76. "The sting of death is sin, but thanks be to God who giveth us the: *victory.*"

77. "To him that knoweth to do good, and doeth it not, to him it is: *sin.*"

78. "The gift of God is eternal: *life.*"

79. "Ye are my friends if ye do: *whatsoever I command you.*"

80. "True worshippers shall worship the Father: *in spirit and in truth.*"

XI. Who Am I?

THIS IS A SERIES of Old Testament biographical questions. Call for the answer at the end of each paragraph. Allow one hundred points if the answer is given at the end of the first paragraph, seventy-five points at the end of the second, fifty at the end of the third, and only twenty-five if the correct answer is not given until all four paragraphs have been read. Correct answers are given in italics.

1. I was the chief priest of Moses as he led the children of Israel out of Egypt. Who am I? (100 points.)

I was a close kin of Moses, the great deliverer. Who am I? (75 points.)

I was the chief spokesman for Moses as he led the children of Israel out of Egypt. Who am I? (50 points.)

I was the temporary leader of the children of Israel when Moses went to Mount Sinai to receive the Ten Commandments. I failed Jehovah and Moses when I let them make and worship a golden calf. Who am I? (25 points.)

I am Aaron.

2. I was a great man who lived in a small town called Ophrah, situated on the west side of the river Jordan in the territory of Manasseh. I was respected for my great strength and fearless courage in battle. Who am I? (100 points.)

I was asked to be king, but declined. I wanted only a few golden earrings. Who am I? (75 points.)

I am the one who is given credit for defeating the great army of the Midianites by going at night to their camp with three hundred of my own soldiers, who blew trumpets, shouted loudly, and flashed glaring flares and torches in the enemy's face. Who am I? (50 points.)

My name begins with the letter "G." Who am I? (25 points.)

I am Gideon.

3. My father was a hundred and eighty-two years old when I was born. I was five hundred years old when my first child was born. I lived nine hundred and fifty years. Who am I? (100 points.)

I am tenth in descent from Adam. I am a righteous man. Who am I? (75 points.)

I am the discoverer of the art of making wine. I am the first person to fall a victim to intoxication. I am a grandson of Methuselah, a son of Lamech. I am the father of three sons: Ham, Shem, and Japheth. Who am I? (50 points.)

God destroyed all other human creatures by a flood except my wife and me, and my three sons and their wives. I built the Ark. Who am I? (25 points.)

I am Noah.

4. I rode upon camels and followed the man, and went his way. I asked: "What man is this that walketh in the fields to meet us?" I was given a ring and bracelets. Who am I? (100 points.)

I am the daughter of Bethuel. I gave food and lodging to a servant and his camels. I am first mentioned in Genesis 22:23. Who am I? (75 points.)

Deborah was my nurse. My great beauty was a source of danger to my husband. I have two sons who are twins. My brother's name was Laban. Who am I? (50 points.)

My husband's name was Isaac. I loved my son Jacob better than my son Esau. I put goatskin on my son's arms and neck to deceive his father, in order that my son would receive the blessing of his father. I helped my son Jacob flee to another land. Who am I? (25 points.)

I am Rebekah.

5. I married my half-brother. I was very beautiful. I was a hundred and twenty-seven years old when I died. I

died twenty-eight years before my husband died. Who am I? (100 points.)

I was buried in the cave of Machpelah. I pretended to be my husband's sister while we were in Egypt. Pharaoh did not know I was married, and he wanted me to become his wife. Who am I? (75 points.)

An Egyptian girl named Hagar was my handmaid. I became angry with my handmaid and sent her away. Who am I? (50 points.)

My first and only child was born when I was ninety-one years old. My son's name was Isaac. My husband's name was Abraham. Who am I? (25 points.)

I am Sarah.

6. I am called the mother of the Arabians. My descendants had charge of David's sheep. Saint Paul refers to me as the type of the Old Covenant, likening me unto Mount Sinai, the Mountain of the Law. In Mohammedan tradition, I am represented as the wife of Abraham. Who am I? (100 points.)

I am an Egyptian mother of one son. Once my son and I were in the wilderness of Beersheba, with nothing but bread and a bottle of water for food. When we had consumed the water, I cast my son under a shrub, expecting him to die. An angel of God called to me. A well of water appeared before me, and I gave my son a drink. Who am I? (75 points.)

My mistress was jealous of me. She mistreated me, so I fled from her dwelling place. I took refuge in the wilderness of Shur, between Philistia and Egypt. I was sent back by the angel of the Lord, and soon after my return I gave birth to a son. Who am I? (50 points.)

Later my mistress had a son, Isaac. She continued to be jealous of me and my sons, and persuaded her husband, Abraham, to send us away. We dwelt in the wilderness of Param. I was Sarah's Egyptian handmaid. My son's name

69

was Ishmael. His father was Abraham. Who am I? (25 points.)

I am Hagar.

7. I did as Moses commanded and fought Amalek. I am the son of Nun. I was one of the scouts sent out by Moses. Who am I? (100 points.)

I was told by both the Lord and Moses to be strong and of good courage. I was told the Lord would be with me, as he was with Moses. I commanded the army that conquered Jericho. Who am I? (75 points.)

I was appointed to take the place of Moses. I divided the land among the people according to the will of Jehovah. I had a camp at Gilgal. Who am I? (50 points.)

I made the sun to stand still. I was buried in Ephraim. Who am I? (25 points.)

I am Joshua.

8. I escaped from my enemies many times. Once I covered a dummy with bedclothes and escaped out the window. The words, "The arrows are way beyond you, run quickly and find them," were my cue to be gone at another time. Who am I? (100 points.)

Because I was a man of war, I could not see my dearest wish carried out. I poured out water as a sacrifice to God. My best friend was my wife's brother. Who am I? (75 points.)

I have been armor-bearer, captain, and musician for my king, who is also my father-in-law. I was a shepherd of Bethlehem. Who am I? (50 points.)

I am a son of Jesse. I have many children. Dearest to me was Absalom. Solomon succeeded me as king. When a boy, I slew Goliath, the Philistine giant. Who am I? (25 points.)

I am David.

9. My father was a very jealous king, and his love for me turned to hate. One day, in his wrath, he attempted to kill me. Who am I? (100 points.)

For some time my father and I carried on war with the Philistines with success. Who am I? (75 points.)

I was slain in the Battle of Gilboa. Who am I? (50 points.)

I neglected to mention that the friendship that existed between David and me was wonderful, passing the love between man and woman. Who am I? (25 points.)

I am Jonathan.

10. I am the handsome son of a great ruler. I loved to pose as the defender of the poor against the oppression of the rich. In this way, I gained the friendship of many poor people. Who am I? (100 points.)

When I felt I could count upon a sufficient number of followers, I left Jerusalem and went to Hebron on the pretext of there making a sacrifice to Jehovah, but really to start a campaign against my father. Who am I? (75 points.)

Although my father loved me better than all his other sons, he was overjoyed at the birth of Solomon and promised to make him heir to his throne instead of me. Who am I? (50 points.)

I was defeated in my campaign against my father and, as I fled, my hair caught in the branch of a tree. The animal I was riding became frightened and ran away, and I was left hanging there. My enemies found me and killed me with their spears. Who am I? (25 points.)

I am Absalom.

11. My brother and I were born near Beersheba, a land settled by my grandfather many years before. Although I was not the firstborn son of my father, I ruled over my brother. Who am I? (100 points.)

I spent several years of my life with my uncle and his family, and later married two of my cousins. When I had acquired large herds, I returned to my homeland. Who am I? (75 points.)

Perhaps I should have mentioned that my uncle was not exactly fair to me, for after I had served seven years to get

71

permission to marry his younger daughter he gave me the older daughter instead, and I had to serve seven more years for the younger daughter. Who am I? (50 points.)

However, my uncle merely turned the tables on me, for I cheated my brother out of his birthright when I gave him in exchange a dish of pottage. Who am I? (25 points.)

I am Jacob.

12. I did not care for warfare, but preferred my flocks. I finally relinquished the faith of Jehovah. No judge, no prophet, no hero of my tribe has been handed down to us. Who am I? (100 points.)

During the journey through the wilderness, my camp was on the south side of the Tabernacle. Arriving on the open downs east of the Jordan, my tribe wished to settle there with their cattle. Moses agreed to let us settle there, after being assured we would still fulfil our part in the conquest of the western country, the land of Canaan proper. Who am I? (75 points.)

It was due to my kindhearted intervention that Joseph, my father's favorite, was not killed but instead was sold into slavery. It was I who agreed to take full responsibility for Benjamin's safety when Joseph later asked that he be brought before him in Egypt. Who am I? (50 points.)

I had two half-brothers named Joseph and Benjamin. I was the first son of Leah and Jacob. My name is used in a song in which the world is supposed to become a grand place if all the women are transported far beyond the deep-blue sea. Who am I? (25 points.)

I am Reuben.

13. I am very beautiful. I was the second daughter of my father. I was the second wife of my husband. I had two sons. Who am I? (100 points.)

I married my cousin. My husband loved me very much. My sons became highly respected, particularly the elder. I died giving birth to my younger son. Who am I? (75 points.)

72

I met my future husband at a watering place. He waited seven years for me and then married my sister. Who am I? (50 points.)

My father-in-law was Isaac. My sons were Joseph and Benjamin. Who am I? (25 points.)

I am Rachel.

14. I am a statesman active in the affairs of Judah. I am a man of great wealth and personal possessions. I am an enthusiast for the law of the Lord and a firm believer in a God of war. My autobiography is found in the Bible. Who am I? (100 points.)

When I was with other people in captivity and was serving in a high position in the court of the King, I kept in close contact with the people of my own city of Jerusalem. News came to me that deplorable conditions existed. I knew I must go to Jerusalem. Who am I? (75 points.)

At the bold risk of losing my position and at great personal sacrifice, I made my request known to the king, who granted my request. I started out with an escort of a captain of the army and horseman, and in due time arrived at Jerusalem as the newly appointed governor. Who am I? (50 points.)

Three days after my arrival, I mounted my horse and at night I went quietly and looked over the walls of the city and found them ruined, as reported. I was ready to call an assembly and explain my motives in returning to their city. The people having a mind to work, my prayers and mission were fulfilled, and the walls were rebuilt. Who am I? (25 points.)

I am Nehemiah.

15. I was driven from my land because of a famine. I am the mother of two sons. I said: "The hand of Jehovah is gone forth against me." Who am I? (100 points.)

The people of my own land did not recognize me upon my return. I sold my property to my kinsman. I changed my name. My husband and two sons had died. Who am I? (75 points.)

I kissed the two women, and they lifted up their voices and wept. My two sons married women of Moab. I have a kinsman whose name is Boaz. My grandson's name is Obed. Who am I? (50 points.)

One of my daughters-in-law would not leave me, and together we went back to Bethlehem. My daughter-in-law gleaned in the fields. She married Boaz. Who am I? (25 points.)

I am Naomi.

16. I was the son of my mother's answered prayer. When I was a very young child, my mother took me to the house of Jehovah, at Shiloh. I was dedicated to the temple service, where I assisted Eli. My mother made me a little robe and brought it to me from year to year, when she came up with her yearly sacrifice. Who am I? (100 points.)

In due time, I was warned by Jehovah of the coming destruction of Eli's house. After the death of Eli and the return of the ark from the Philistines, I became judge of Israel and called the people to repentance at Mizpah, and saved them from the invading Philistines. Who am I? (75 points.)

I was sent to the home of Jesse to select and appoint a successor to Saul. I chose David. Who am I? (50 points.)

My father was Elkanah, and my mother was Hannah. My successor was Saul, the first King of Israel. Two books of the Old Testament bear my name. Who am I? (25 points.)

I am Samuel.

17. I am a son of Rebekah and an ancestor of the Edomites. Who am I? (100 points.)

I am a great man of the out-of-doors. I like to hunt and roam the fields and mountains. Who am I? (75 points.)

I am very hairy. I sold my birthright to my brother for a bowl of soup. Who am I? (50 points.)

74

I have a twin brother by the name of Jacob. My name begins with the letter E. Who am I? (25 points.)

I am Esau.

18. As a man, I am self-restrained. As a soldier. I am brave and devoted. I am an officer in David's army under Joab. Who am I? (100 points.)

I was sent with some brave men to a place near the wall of the city, where the enemies would kill me. I slept at the door of the King's house, rather than go to my own. Who am I? (75 points.)

I carried a letter that contained my own death sentence. I am a Hittite and one of David's thirty mighty men. Who am I? (50 points.)

I was the husband of Bathsheba. The King rewarded my faithful service with injustice and death. Who am I? (25 points.)

I am Uriah.

19. I am overbearing, vindictive, able, and unscrupulous. My husband, who was king, took second place. He, a man of weak will, was the passive instrument of my stronger nature. Who am I? (100 points.)

I ordered the death of Naboth, owner of a neighboring vineyard, because he would not sell his vineyard to the King. I established the religion of Baal in Israel. I persecuted and tried to exterminate the prophets of Israel. Who am I? (75 points.)

I threatened the life of Elijah, until he fled from Israel into the wilderness of Beersheba for a time, to escape death at my hand. I was the daughter of King of Tyre, who was a priest of the religion of Baal. I was the wife of Ahab, King of Israel. Who am I? (50 points.)

I met a tragic death at the hand of Jehu. Dogs ate my flesh. Who am I? (25 points.)

I am Jezebel.

20. On behalf of Jehovah, I had the courage to stand up singly against the whole power of the kingdom. I told the

King there would be neither dew nor rain these years except by my word. I rested in a cave one night. Who am I? (100 points.)

Accused of causing the death of the widow's son, I took him and prayed that God would return the soul of the boy, and the boy lived and was restored to his mother. While sleeping in the wilderness, I was twice awakened by an angel and told to eat, and I found food and water beside me. Who am I? (75 points.)

I was fed by the ravens while I dwelt by the brook Cherith. I was fed for some time by a widow, who had but a handful of meal and a little oil when I went to her house; but I told her that Jehovah said the meal and oil would not fail while the drought lasted. By God's sending fire down to consume his sacrifice, I proved on Mount Carmel before the people of Israel that Jehovah was God. Who am I? (50 points.)

I anointed Elisha to be my successor as prophet. When we came to the river Jordan, I took my mantle, wrapped it together, and struck the waters so that they parted, and Elisha and I crossed over on dry ground. Who am I? (25 points.)

I am Elijah.

21. When I took over the kingdom of Israel, I fought against all my enemies on every side—against Moab, against the children of Ammon, against the kings of Zobah, against the Philistines, and against the Amalekites. Who am I? (100 points.)

I was advised by my servants to employ music as a relief from a mental trouble, called an evil spirit from the Lord. The servants suggested that I get David to play for me. David played the harp. I was refreshed, and the evil spirit departed from me. I loved David greatly, and he became my armor-bearer. Who am I? (75 points.)

In despair, I once applied to the witch at Endor, but received only a hopeless message. My sons were slain. I called upon my armor-bearer to slay me, but he refused. I fell upon my own sword and died. Who am I? (50 points.)

I was the son of Kish. I was selected the first King of Israel. Who am I? (25 points).

I am Saul.

22. I was born in the land of Canaan and was the eleventh of twelve sons of a great patriarch. Who am I? (100 points.)

When I became a man, I served the Pharoah in Egypt by being a great administrator in that country. Who am I? (75 points.)

I prevented a famine in Egypt. I was a great interpreter of dreams. In my youth, I was a slave in Egypt. Who am I? (50 points.)

My father, Jacob, gave me a coat of many colors before I was sold into slavery by my brothers, but I forgave them of their wrongdoing and blessed them all. Who am I? (25 points.)

I am Joseph.

23. I was born near Beersheba, where my parents had settled after many years of wandering. My parents were very happy when I was born, for they had long before given up hope of having an heir. Who am I? (100 points.)

Later, when I was old enough to marry, my father sent one of his oldest servants back to his homeland to find a wife for me. Fortunately, the servant brought back exactly the type of girl my father had sent him to find, and we were happily married. Twin sons were born to us, but as they grew older it became apparent that, although they were twins, they were not alike. One son spent his time in the open—hunting, trapping, and caring for the sheep—while the other rarely strayed away from the house. Who am I? (75 points.)

When I grew old and sent for my son Esau to bless him as my heir, Jacob, with the help of his mother, deceived me and received my blessing instead. Who am I? (50 points.)

I neglected to tell you that my father, Abraham, was prepared to offer me as a sacrifice when suddenly he noticed a ram caught by its horns in a thorn tree and used it instead. Who am I? (25 points.)

I am Isaac.

24. I was a civil and military leader in Israel. The Lord made me have dominion over the mighty. I lived between Ramah and Bethel on Mt. Ephraim. The children of Israel came to me for judgment. Who am I? (100 points.)

A great battle was fought during my time as judge. The leader of my army pursued the chariots of my enemy and killed all but the leader, who fled. After the battle my land had rest for forty years. Who am I? (75 points.)

The leader of my army would not go to battle unless I went along. I told him that the glory of the expedition would not be his. The captured leader of my enemy's army asked for water and was given milk. Who am I? (50 points.)

My husband's name was Lapidoth. The wife of Heber killed the leader of my enemy's army with a tent pin. The leader of my army was Barak. I was succeeded by Gideon as judge. I was a prophetess. My name begins with the letter D. Who am I? (25 points.)

I am Deborah.

25. I am the son of Elkanah, and I made my home in the city of Ramah. I grew up to be a leader of my people and told them of God. Who am I? (100 points.)

I was the fifteenth and last judge of Israel. I was a lover of peace, but at one time I was forced to battle some invaders of our land. Through God's help, we were able to overcome our enemies. At the place of victory I placed a stone, calling it Ebenezer, which means "the stone of help." Who am I? (75 points.)

When I grew old, I appointed my sons to be judges in my place; but they were unsatisfactory, and the people asked for a king. This was sad news to me. However, God answered my bewildering prayers with comfort and pointed out to me the person to be made king. I anointed Saul, the first King of Israel. Who am I? (50 points.)

I was reared in a temple by a priest. My mother promised that if she might have a son she would dedicate him to the work of the Lord. God spoke to me one night when I was but a child. Who am I? (25 points.)

I am Samuel.

26. I performed many miracles, which occurred at a time when the religion of Jehovah was struggling for existence against Baal worship. In the name of the Lord, I healed with salt the waters of the spring of Jericho. I predicted the birth of a son to a Shunamite woman, and at my prayer that son was restored to life after he had died. Who am I? (100 points).

I made an iron axhead that had fallen into the river float to the surface. I informed Benhadah, King of Syria, of his approaching death. I declared the destruction of Ahab and his whole house. Who am I? (75 points.)

I was one of two great proprets of the older period of Israelite history. I used my miraculous power largely in simple deeds of kindness. After my death, a man hastily cast into the same sepulcher was at once restored to life on touching my bones. Who am I? (50 points.)

I was plowing, and a great prophet came and cast his mantle over me. When this prophet went beyond Jordan to be translated to heaven, I kept by him. I asked for a double portion of the prophet's spirit as a parting gift. A fiery chariot took my master away, and his mantle fell on me. I struck the Jordan with it, and the waters divided, permitting me to cross. God appointed me to succeed the prophet Elijah. Who am I? (25 points.)

I am Elisha.

27. I was the son of Terah, who lived beyond the valley of the Euphrates River. Who am I? (100 points.)

My name means "father of a multitude." People seem to know very little of my last days, but at the age of a hundred and seventy-five I passed away and was placed with my wife, Sarah, is the tomb of Machpelah. My second wife, Keturah, was not nearly so beautiful as my first wife. Who am I? (75 points.)

When my son, Isaac, had matured, I sent out my servant to find Isaac a wife. He returned with the very beautiful and able Rebekah. Who am I? (50 points.)

I am referred to as the father of the Hebrew race. Who am I? (25 points.)

I am Abraham.

28. My name means "mistress." I had weak eyes. When my husband married my younger sister, the love I had for her changed to hatred, because I grew jealous of her beauty. Who am I? (100 points.)

Before my husband could marry me, my father made him work for the family without pay for seven years, passing it off as the custom of the land. There is mention of this piece of stratagem in Genesis 29. Who am I? (75 points.)

After marrying me, my husband had to work seven more years for my father, Laban, before he could marry my younger sister. Who am I? (50 points.)

I was greatly grieved by my husband's partiality to my beautiful sister, Rachel, but I devoted most of my time to my children. Who am I? (25 points.)

I am Leah.

29. I was one of the judges of Israel and a popular hero

in my time. I belonged to the tribe of Dan, and my judging days lasted twenty years. Who am I? (100 points.)

I married the daughter of one of the Philistines. I caused my wife's people many perplexities by my riddles and practical jokes. I once went on a journey to Ackalon, where I killed thirty people to pay for one of my riddles. Who am I? (75 points.)

I soon saw another beautiful girl whom I loved. A popular opera today is named after us. By trickery, this woman discovered the secret of my great strength, which lay in my hair. She betrayed me to the Philistines. Who am I? (50 points.)

The Philistines hadn't reckoned that my hair would grow again, and with it my strength. So I got revenge upon Delilah and her people by destroying a huge temple while they were making sport of me. Who am I? (25 points.)

I am Samson.

30. I was the son of Jephunneh, and I represent the tribe of Judah. A tribe of people who afterward became associated with the tribe of Judah was named for me. Who am I? (100 points.)

I am one of the champions of Jehovah because I was faithful to him. I have been called a great spy. Who am I? (75 points.)

Together with another, I was sent into the land of Canaan to see if the land was ready for invasion. I advocated immediate attack on the land. Who am I? (50 points.)

My fellow spy was Joshua. Who am I? (25 points.)

I am Caleb.

31. I am one of the most remarkable men of Jewish history. I regard my enemies as God's enemies. I was prepared for my career by my experiences in many battles as a soldier. I was made commander of the army and later ruler of the land. Who am I? (100 points.)

I was selected as a representative of my tribe to be one

of the twelve spies. I commanded the sun and moon to stand still. Who am I? (75 points.)

I was the son of Nun, of the twelfth generation after Joseph. I was told to choose men and to go out and fight with Amalek. Who am I? (50 points.)

I was chosen to lead the people into Canaan. I captured Jericho. My great work was the conquest and settlement of Palestine. Who am I? (25 points.)

I am Joshua.

32. I was compelled to leave Egypt, so I fled to Midian. I was sent unto my people to help them. My son's name was Gershom. Who am I? (100 points.)

My mother made extraordinary efforts for my preservation. My sister was anxious about my fate. I was adopted by a princess. For many years, I was considered an Egyptian. Who am I? (75 points.)

Zipporah was my wife. I was slow of speech. I did all that Jehovah commanded me. Who am I? (50 points.)

I gave the Ten Commandments. I am portrayed as a leader and a lawgiver. Aaron, who was my brother, was a great inspiration to me in my work. Who am I? (25 points.)

I am Moses.

33. I was King of Samaria for twenty-two years. I displeased God by making an altar for Baal in Samaria. It was my wife who first introduced the worship of Baal. Who am I? (100 points.)

My father was Omri. I did more to provoke God than all the kings of Israel before me. I built some cities, an ivory house, and a sepulcher. Who am I? (75 points.)

I married Jezebel, daughter of the King of Zidon. Who am I? (50 points.)

I wanted Naboth's vineyard near my palace, which he had inherited from his father and would not sell. I was very angry about this, and my wife persuaded me to kill Naboth and take the vineyard. Who am I? (25 points.)

I am Ahab.

82

XII. Is It in the Bible?

IN CERTAIN INSTANCES, more than the number called for are named. All the answers given are correct.

1. Name three precious stones mentioned in the Bible: *agate, emerald, diamond, jasper, amethyst, ruby, topaz, sapphire, onyx.*

2. Name three mountains mentioned in the Bible: *Ararat, Abarim, Bashan, Nebo, Olives, Bethel, Gilboa, Hermon, Zion, Pisgah, Sinai.*

3. Name three rivers in the Bible: *Kidron, Chebar, Euphrates, Nile, Jordan, Kishon, Kanah.*

4. Name three musical instruments in the Bible: *harp, cornet, flute, organ, timbrel, trumpet, cymbal, viol, dulcimer.*

5. Name three diseases mentioned in the Bible: *leprosy, palsy, epilepsy, plague, boils, consumption, fever, deafness.*

6. Name three reptiles mentioned in the Bible: *asp, adder, crocodile, dragon, lizard, serpent, scorpion, frog, viper, turtle.*

7. Name three domestic animals mentioned in the Bible: *lamb, goat, ram, horse, ox, camel, swine, dog.*

8. Name three fruits mentioned in the Bible: *apple, grape, fig, pomegranate, raisins, olive.*

9. Name three wild animals mentioned in the Bible: *lion, rabbit, lizard, mole, fox, weasel, ferret, snail, bear.*

10. Name three trees mentioned in the Bible: *sycamore, cypress, fig, fir, almond, cedar, bay, olive, acacia, ash.*

11. Name three birds mentioned in the Bible: *owl, swallow, dove, sparrow, raven, eagle, quail, pelican, pigeon.*

12. Name three women of very early Bible history: *Sarah, Hagar, Jochebed.*

13. Name three men of very early Bible history: *Adam, Lot, Noah, etc.*

14. Name three men of the New Testament other than disciples: *Nicodemus, Lazarus, Cornelius, etc.*

15. Name three women of the New Testament: *Mary, Salome, Priscilla.*

16. Name three kings before the division of the kingdom: *Saul, David, Solomon.*

17. Name three kings of Israel after the division of the kingdom: *Jeroboam, Ahab, Jehu.*

18. Name three kings of Judah after the division of the kingdom: *Rehoboam, Asa, Joash, Hezekiah.*

19. Name three monarchs of foreign nations: *Cyrus, Hiram, Sennacherib.*

20. Name three queens mentioned in the Bible: *Sheba, Candace, Vashti.*

21. Name three great leaders of Israel: *Moses, Joshua, Ezra.*

22. Name three army commanders mentioned in the Bible: *Gideon, Joab, Abner.*

23. Name three judges mentioned in the Bible: *Samson, Deborah, Jephtah.*

24. Name three major prophets mentioned in the Bible: *Isaiah, Jeremiah, Ezekiel.*

25. Name three shepherds mentioned in the Bible: *Abel, Moses, David.*

26. Name three tillers of the soil mentioned in the Bible: *Cain, Isaac, Noah.*

27. Name three exceptionally wicked women mentioned in the Bible: *Jezebel, Athaliah, Herodias.*

28. Name three beautiful women mentioned in the Bible: *Bathsheba, Vashti, Esther.*

29. Name three very rich men mentioned in the Bible: *Abraham, Solomon, Job.*

30. Name three missionaries mentioned in the Bible: *Paul, Philip, Barnabas.*

31. Name three lepers mentioned in the Bible: *Naaman, Gehazi, Uzziah.*

32. Name three young men honored in foreign lands: *Joseph, Daniel, Nehemiah.*

33. Name three minor prophets mentioned in the Bible: *Hosea, Joel, Amos.*

34. Name three children mentioned in the Bible: *Naaman's little maid, the boy with the loaves and fishes, Jairus' daughter.*

35. Name three skillful hunters mentioned in the Bible: *Nimrod, Esau, Samson.*

36. Name three persons raised from the dead: *Lazarus, the Shunammite's son, Dorcas.*

37. Name the three persons who performed these miracles: *Christ, Elisha, Peter.*

38. Name three countries of Old Testament times: *Canaan, Egypt, Assyria.*

39. Name three countries of New Testament times: *Greece, Italy, Macadonia.*

40. Name two pairs of loyal friends: *David and Jonathan, Ruth and Naomi.*

XIII. Bible Conundrums

THESE QUESTIONS are Bible Question Bee interludes. They are solely for fun. The answers should not be scored in a question-and-answer contest.

1. Who was the greatest orator spoken of in the Bible? *Samson, because he brought the house down.*

2. When was paper currency spoken of first in the Bible? *When the dove left the ark and brought a green back.*

3. What proof have we that Moses was the most wicked man who ever lived? *Because he broke the Ten Commandments all at once.*

4. Who was the fastest runner? *Adam, because he was first in the race.*

5. What three words did Adam use when he introduced himself to Eve, which read backward and forward the same? *"Madam, I'm Adam."*

6. Who was the straightest man mentioned in the Bible? *Joseph, because Pharaoh made a ruler of him.*

7. What evidence have we that Adam used sugar? *Because he raised Cain.*

8. Who first introduced salt meat into the Navy? *Noah, when he took Ham into the Ark.*

9. What man mentioned in the Bible had no father? *Joshua, the son of Nun.*

10. Name two noblemen in the Bible. *"Barren Fig Tree" and "Lord How Long."*

XIV. A Bible Question Bee Review

1. For what did Esau sell his birthright? *For a mess of pottage.*

2. Who betrayed Samson? *Delilah.*

3. To whom did God give the Ten Commandments? *Moses.*

4. How did Stephen die? *He was stoned to death.*

5. What daughter of what king did David marry? *Michal, daughter of King Saul.*

6. Who was Solomon's father? *David.*

7. Whom did Pharaoh appoint in charge of food during the famine in Egypt? *Joseph.*

8. Who was the youngest brother of Joseph? *Benjamin.*

9. What was the name of Joseph's oldest brother? *Reuben.*

10. What was the name of the valley where David slew Goliath? *Elah.*

11. What food did John the Baptist eat while he was in the wilderness? *Locusts and wild honey.*

12. What is the last book of the Old Testament? *Malachi.*

13. What is the last book of the New Testament? *Revelation.*

14. How were Simon and Andrew related? *They were brothers.*

15. What trade did Jesus learn as a boy? *Carpenter.*

16. Complete—"Resist the devil: *and he will flee from you.*"

17. Complete the following quotation: "Behold, the Lamb of God: *that taketh away the sin of the world.*"

18. Complete the following quotation: "Though your sins be as scarlet: *they shall be as white as snow.*"

19. Complete the following quotation: "Greater love hath no man than this: *that a man lay down his life for his friends.*"

20. Complete the following quotation: "Why call ye me Lord, Lord: *and do not the things which I say?*"

21. Who was Joseph's mother? *Rachel.*

22. Who was called "the lawgiver of the Israelites"? *Moses.*

23. Quote the first part of the Fifth Commandment. *"Honor thy father and thy mother."*

24. Who was the mother of John the Baptist? *Elizabeth.*

25. Who were the friends of Jesus in Bethany? *Mary, Martha, and Lazarus.*

26. To whom was the Sermon on the Mount addressed? *Jesus' disciples.*

27. Who was the physician in the New Testament? *Luke.*

28. Who was the child king in the Old Testament, and how old was he? *Josiah, at the age of eight.*

29. What was the greatest friendship in the Bible? *David and Jonathan.*

30. Who was Moses' sister? Miriam.

31. What are the first five books of the Bible called? *The Pentateuch.*

32. Who was called the wisest king? *Solomon.*

33. How were the Israelites fed in the wilderness? *Manna.*

34. When God spoke to Moses in the burning bush, what did he tell Moses to do? *To go to Egypt and bring the Israelites out.*

35. Who said: "Man that is born of woman is of few days and full of trouble"? *Job.*

36. Who said: "Verily I say unto you, one of you which eateth with me shall betray me"? *Jesus.*

37. Which is the shortest Psalm? *Psalm 117.*

38. Who was Jacob's favorite son? *Joseph.*

39. How long were the Israelites in the wilderness? *Forty years.*

40. Who were Elimelech's wife and daughters-in-law? *Naomi, his wife; and Ruth and Orpah, his daughters-in-law.*

41. Who was the son of Abraham and Hagar, cast out by Sarah? *Ishmael.*

42. Who accompanied Paul on the first missionary journey? *Barnabas.*

43. In what land did Job live? *Uz.*

44. What aged Jew blessed the infant Jesus in the temple? *Simeon.*

45. Of what country was King Hiram, who helped Solomon collect material for the temple? *Tyre.*

46. By what name was Jacob known in his later years? *Israel.*

47. Which of Namoi's daughter-in-laws did not return with her? *Orpah.*

48. Who was called "a mighty hunter"? *Nimrod.*

49. Name the three famous Johns of the New Testament. *John the Baptist, John the Apostle, and John Mark.*

50. Complete the following quotation from Proverbs: "A wise son maketh: *a glad father."*

51. What city was capital of the Assyrian Empire? *Nineveh.*

52. What blind beggar was given sight by Jesus near Jericho? *Bartimaeus.*

53. Who was priest when the child Samuel was taken to the temple? *Eli.*

54. To what village were two disciples walking when Jesus walked and talked with them after the resurrection? *Emmaus.*

55. Who said: "I know that my Redeemer liveth and at last he will stand up upon the earth"? *Job.*

56. What tribe of Israel received no portion of the land divided among the Israelites? *Levi.*

57. What did Peter answer when Jesus asked: "Who say ye that I am?" *"Thou are the Christ."*

58. Complete the following quotation: "God is a Spirit, and they that worship him must: *worship him in spirit and in truth."*

59. Complete the following quotation: "An eye for an: *eye and a tooth for a tooth."*

60. Complete these words of Peter: "Silver and gold have I none, but: *what I have, that give I thee."*

61. Complete the following quotation: "As Moses lifted up the serpent in the wilderness, even: *so must the Son of Man be lifted up."*

62. What did the priests of Israel carry in their hands as they marched around the walls of Jericho? *Trumpets.*

63. What did the ark of the covenant contain? *The Book of the Law, the Covenant, Aaron's rod, and for a while a pot of manna.*

64. What is the name of the chief river of Palestine? *Jordan.*

65. How often were Hebrew pilgrimages made to Jerusalem for the Feast of the Passover? *Annually.*

66. How long was the Egyptian captivity? *About four hundred years.*

67. For how many pieces of silver was Jesus betrayed? *Thirty.*

68. To what great man of the Old Testament did God appear in a burning bush? *Moses.*

69. What tree was the glory of the Palestinian forests, symbol of grandeur and loftiness? *The cedar.*

70. By what trade did the Apostle Paul support himself? *He was a tent maker.*

71. What part did Saul have in the stoning of Stephen? *He cared for the garments of those who did the stoning.*

72. At whose tomb did Jesus weep? *Lazarus'.*

73. Who asked the widow of Nain to make him a little cake of meal? *Elijah.*

74. Who was let down a city's walls in a basket that he might escape? *Paul.*

75. Whose words are these, and to whom were they spoken: "It is hard to kick gainst the pricks"? *Jesus, to Saul of Tarsus.*

76. To whom did the prophet Nathan say these words: "Thou art the man"? *David.*

77. Who said: "Saul, Saul, why persecutest thou me?" *Jesus.*

78. Who went into the most holy place of the temple, alone and but once a year? *The high priest.*

79. Complete the following quotation: "Faith is the substance of things hoped for, the evidence of: *things not seen.*"

80. What time was the ninth hour? *Four P.M.*

81. How many days after the Passover was Pentecost? *Fifty.*

82. The city of Tarsus was the birthplace of what noted Bible character? *Paul, or Saul of Tarsus.*

83. What famous teacher in Jerusalem taught Saul of Tarsus? *Gamaliel.*

84. What is a centurion? *An officer in the Roman army commanding one hundred men.*

85. Who wrote the Book of Acts? *Luke.*

86. Who was called the "weeping prophet"? *Jeremiah.*

87. Who got a chance to become great by crying at the proper time? *Moses.*

88. What is it that cannot be bought, yet is worth more than rubies? *Wisdom.*

89. What kings ruled over all the tribes of Israel? *Saul, David, and Solomon.*

91

90. Who was called "the great singer of Israel"? *David*.

91. What men compared themselves to grasshoppers? *Ten of the spies who went to spy out the Promised Land*.

92. What other spies besides Joshua gave a favorable report and wanted to go on to possess the Promised Land? *Caleb*.

93. What prophet learned a lesson from a worm? *Jonah*.

94. In whose marriage did an old shoe play an important part? *That of Ruth and Boaz*.

95. What man planned to hang his enemy but had to honor him instead, and who was his enemy? *Haman and Mordecai*.

96. Who was called "this dreamer"? *Joseph*.

97. Whom did Jesus call "sons of thunder"? *James and John*.

98. Who was king when David fought Goliath? *Saul*.

99. Who was king when the Queen of Sheba came to visit Solomon? *Solomon*.

100. Who was king when the Assyrian army was smitten by the angel of Jehovah? *Hezekiah*.

101. Who was king when Elijah had his great contest with the priests of Baal on Mount Carmel? *Ahab*.

102. Who said: "Am I my brother's keeper"? *Cain*.

103. Who said: "Here am I; send me"? *Isaiah*.

104. What are the first words of Jesus recorded in the Bible? *"How is it that ye sought me? Wist ye not that I must be about my Father's business?"*

105. Who led the children of Israel out of Egyptian bondage? *Moses*.

106. While moving the ark of the covenant, what man, thinking it was going to fall, put up his hand to steady it and fell dead? *Uzza(h)*.

107. After Jesus arose from the tomb, how long did he remain on earth before he ascended? *Forty days*.

108. Who was Abraham's second wife? *Keturah*.

109. Who was Jacob's daughter? *Dinah*.

110. What woman made garments for the poor? *Dorcas.*

111. Where was the Apostle John when he wrote the Book of Revelation? *On the isle of Patmos.*

112. How many times were the Ten Commandments given to Moses? *Twice.*

113. How many missionary journeys did Paul make? *Three.*

114. What persecutor of Christians was converted after being struck blind by a bright light? *Saul of Tarsus, afterward called Paul.*

115. Who made the golden calf? *Aaron.*

116. Who was killed with a shepherd's sling? *Goliath.*

117. Who had boils? *Job.*

118. Who saw the handwriting on the wall? *Belshazzar.*

119. Who played the harp before King Saul? *David.*

120. Who sold his birthright for something to eat? *Esau.*

121. Who was cast into a lion's den? *Daniel.*

122. Who with the jawbone of an ass slew many men? *Samson.*

123. Who lay in a basket in the bulrushes? *Moses.*

124. Who hung by the hair of his head? *Absalom.*

125. Who was fed by a flock of ravens? *Elijah.*

126. Who was rebuked by his beast and brought to a halt? *Balaam.*

127. Who looked behind and turned to salt? *Lot's wife.*

128. Who said: "Art thou he that should come or do we look for another?" *John the Baptist.*

129. To whom was this question put: "Whom do ye say that I, the Son of Man, am?" *Jesus' disciples.*

130. Who, when he was dying, said: "Lord, lay not this sin to their charge"? *Stephen.*

131. Whom did God say was a perfect and upright man? *Job.*

132. Who was chosen in Judas' place as disciple? *Mathias.*

133. Who said: "Come, see a man who told me all things I ever did"? *The Woman of Samaria.*

134. What famous rebuke did Jesus once address to Peter? *"Get behind me, Satan."*

135. What was the last plague sent on Pharaoh before he released the children of Israel? *The slaying of the first-born.*

136. Who, when he awoke, said: "Surely God must have been in this place"? *Jacob.*

137. Of Samson's many wonderful feats of strength, which was the greatest? *Pulling down the two pillars of the House of Dagon.*

138. Who posed this riddle: "Out of the eater came forth meat, and out of the strong came forth sweetness"? *Samson.*

139. What verse is known as the *"Golden Text of the Bible"*? *"For God so loved the world that he gave his only begotten Son that whosoever believe in him should not perish but have everlasting life."*

140. What was the Sanhedrin? *The supreme council or court of the Jews.*

141. Who was Mephibosheth? *Jonathan's crippled son.*

142. How do we know Elisha was bald-headed? From the following statement: *"The children mocked him and said, 'Go up, thou bald head.'"*

143. Who was Malchus? *The servant of the high priest who was wounded by Peter.*

144. Who went with Paul on his second missionary journey? *Silas.*

145. From what part of the country did the twelve disciples come? *All came from Galilee except Judas Iscariot, who came from Judea.*

146. Where was Jesus Crucified? *Just outside Jerusalem, at Golgotha.*

147. Quote at least four different statements Jesus made

from the cross. *"Father, forgive them, for they know not what they do." "Today shalt thou be with me in paradise." "Woman, behold thy son; son, behold thy mother." "I thirst." "My God, my God, why hast thou forsaken me?" "It is finished." "Father, into thy hands I commend my spirit."*

148. Who said: "Though I should die with thee, yet will I not deny thee"? *Peter.*

149. Who went on the first missionary journey to Europe? *Barnabas and Paul.*

150. Why did David send Uriah to the front of the army? *Because he wanted to marry Uriah's wife, Bathsheba.*

151. Who was the most afflicted man in the Bible? *Job.*

152. What is the difference between Saul and Paul, both New Testament characters? *They are the same person. Paul was known as Saul until the time of his conversion.*

153. Who was the man who laid at the gate of a certain rich man and would have eaten the crumbs that fell from the rich man's table? *Lazarus.*

154. Who was the woman who permitted the Hebrew spies to lodge in her house? *Rahab.*

155. How did Rahab release the spies? *She let them down through the window by a cord.*

156. Which one of Jesus' disciples was especially impetuous? *Peter.*

157. What was the name of Adam's first child? *Cain.*

158. How long was Moses upon the mount with God? *Forty days and nights.*

159. To whom was the Sermon on the Mount addressed? *Jesus' disciples.*

160. Where did Jesus go immediately after his baptism, and how long did he stay here? *Into the wilderness, for forty days.*

161. Who was the first Gentile convert to Christianity? *Cornelius.*

162. What new commandment did Jesus give? *"A new commandment I give unto you, that you love one another, even as I have loved you, that you also love one another."*

163. What became of the thirty pieces of silver that Judas received for betraying Jesus? *A potter's field in which to bury strangers was purchased with the money after he returned it.*

164. What is faith, according to the Bible? *"The substance of things hoped for, the evidence of things not seen."*

165. What three parables of Jesus are about lost things? *That of the lost sheep, of the lost coin, and of the lost son.*

166. What did Jesus say at the end of his story about the good Samaritan? *"Go and do thou likewise."*

167. What severe test of Abraham's faith was made on Mt. Moriah? *The offering of his son Isaac.*

168. When were the Apostles filled with the holy spirit? *On Pentecost.*

169. What happened to the Egyptians who were following the children of Israel? *They were drowned in the Red Sea.*

170. Who went to Samaria and preached Christ? *Philip.*

171. Of whom was this spoken: "And they were both righteous before God, walking in all the commandments and ordinances of the Lord, blameless"? *Zacharias and Elizabeth.*

172. On what occasion did Jesus utter these words: "Get thee hence, Satan, for it is written, thou shalt worship the Lord thy God and him only shalt thou serve"? *At his temptation in the wilderness.*

173. To whom did Jesus talk concerning the new birth? *Nicodemus.*

174. What did Jesus pray in the Garden of Gethsemane that his followers should pray? *"Not my will, but thine be done."*

175. In what city did Paul find many idols? *Athens.*